THIS JOURNAL, IF USED EVERY DAY, COULD RADICALLY TRANSFORM, PROFOUNDLY SHAPE AND DYNAMICALLY IMPROVE YOUR HEALTH, WELLNESS & VITALITY.

THIS WELLNESS JOURNAL BELONGS TO:

....

On this day ..Monday. Jan 18, '21, I commit to a lifestyle of wellness and vitality and changing what I believe is possible for my health.

Signed:

.........Terry Young.............................

Dailygreatness Wellness Journal: A Holistic Guide to Health, Wellness and Vitality
Created by Lyndelle Palmer-Clarke

Help us spread our transformational journals and planner by sharing your images on social media using #dailygreatnessjournal or review the Dailygreatness Wellness Journal on Amazon or our website and enter our monthly draw to win a free copy for yourself or a friend!

To reorder your Dailygreatness Wellness Journal and browse all our other journals, online courses and content, please visit www.dailygreatnessjournal.com

Dreaming Room Publishing
First Edition Dreaming Room 2016
Design by Viktoryia Nesheva
Printed in China

We recommend consulting your physician before starting any exercise program. Results may vary from person to person as with any personal development program. No express or implied guarantees are made for your personal results through using the Dailygreatness Wellness Journal or purchasing this product.

The goal of this wellness journal is simple: to help you make conscious choices about your health and wellness so you can improve the quality of your life and achieve your goals and dreams.

Our health is the very foundation of our life. Without health, we can't achieve our goals, we fail to be our best for ourselves and the people around us, we feel defeated and powerless to make positive changes, and we fall short of living up to the greatness that lies within us. To improve any area of our life, the first place to start is our health. That's why, of all the journals and planners in the Dailygreatness series, this could be the most powerful. When we improve our health and wellness, we improve our ability to see what's possible for our life, and we have the energy to pursue those possibilities. It's in the pursuit of those possibilities that we find our happiness.

Making improvements to your heath is not difficult, it simply starts with a decision to focus on your wellbeing and to take small actions each day that will improve your health in positive ways. The old idea that health is about focusing only on what you eat and how much you exercise -- doesn't work. This one dimensional way of thinking keeps us stuck; trapped yoyoing back and forth making no real change. While diet and exercise are most definitely important -- you can do it smarter. Thinking of your health holistically is the smart way to creating lasting health, wellness and vitality. When you change your way of thinking and see yourself as a whole person, body, mind and spirit, you uncover the missing link that can help you rapidly improve, not only your wellness but every area of your life.

Improved wellness starts with a willingness to make changes and a belief that you can improve. If you can't conceive that better health is a possibility for you, then no matter what you do regarding food, diet and exercise, you will never experience what optimal health really is.

This journal takes a holistic view of who you are which is why it works. Each day, throughout the next year, you'll be focusing on, not only your body through diet and exercise but your mindset through self-awareness practises and noticing how the thoughts you think, affect your health. You'll be tuning into your intuition and inner wisdom for guidance on what's best for your health and overcome health challenges that perhaps you've not been able to overcome in the past.

Starting and ending your day with the Dailygreatness Wellness Journal will empower you to create your days in new and exciting ways, focus on your potential and live a life of passion, purpose and vitality.

Wishing you unlimited wellness!

Lyndelle

THE BODY-MIND CONNECTION

Creating optimal health in your body, starts with optimal thinking in your mind. Healthy thoughts create healthy behaviours, and your body's health and vitality depends largely on your habitual thinking patterns. You literally create your health and wellness with every thought, every word and every action you take.

Your starting point is self-honesty. By acknowledging and taking responsibility for where you are with your health you gain clarity on what has or has not been serving you and empower yourself to make positive changes for the future. No matter where you are on your health and wellness journey, you can't make progress if you're still beating yourself up for poor choices you've made in the past. You have to accept them, come into the present moment and start exactly where you are. The exciting news is, you have the power to make new choices in every new moment and move beyond past limitations and into optimal health.

All lasting transformations start from within. Over the next year, you'll become aware of the thoughts that are dominating your mind and begin to upgrade them to healthier thoughts that support your new wellness lifestyle. Even if you are already healthy, there is always room for improvement and to optimise your health.

AS YOU THINK HEALTHY, POSITIVE THOUGHTS, YOU WILL NATURALLY MAKE HEALTHY, POSITIVE CHOICES. THE MIND AND BODY ARE CONNECTED -- SO START WITHIN.

PURPOSE AND POTENTIAL

Your purpose is the fuel you need to move you from where you are to where you want to be. To successfully reach your wellness goals, you need to think beyond diet and exercise and see your life holistically. Creating a strong WHY for wanting to improve your health, will help you stay inspired and on track to achieving your wellness goals. Although this is a yearly wellness journal, the goal is to stop thinking short-term and start thinking lifestyle.

To achieve your goals, it is helpful to identify the bigger purpose to your life, a WHY that motivates and excites you and that will serve as your willpower if you are ever tempted to quit. When you have an inspiring purpose, beyond simply how you look in the mirror, you'll find an enthusiasm for life that perhaps you've never had before. Wellness then becomes the vehicle for achieving your purpose in life.

When you know your why, no one or no thing can stop you. You know where you're going, what you need to do and no challenge, difficulty or obstacle can get in your way. When you know your why, you're excited by what's possible, you let go of fear, anxiety and procrastination and easily achieve your goals.

The more energy you have, the better you feel and the easier it is to pursue your bigger goals and to attain optimal health. As you fulfil your purpose and unlock more of your body and mind's potential, you naturally feel happier, more content and even blissful. Health really is the foundation to a happy life.

Soon you'll have a chance to craft your very own Why Statement, designed to motivate and inspire you to achieve your wellness goals.

TRUE HAPPINESS COMES THROUGH REACHING FOR YOUR POTENTIAL.

THE JOURNEY

Holistic health focuses on not only your workouts and food choices but how you think, how you spend your spare time, who you hang out with and the environments you expose yourself to. When your intentions, thoughts and actions are congruent you'll begin to see amazing results in your health and wellness.

Even the smallest of new choices can create huge changes to how you feel in your body and mind.

Each morning session, throughout the journal, is designed to move you into a peak state preparing your body and mind, so you are ready to take massive action on your wellness goals. Each evening session is designed for reflecting on your day, becoming conscious of your strengths, noticing what you'd like to work on and where you might be sabotaging yourself.

As you see your transformation unfold over the weeks and months ahead, you'll be inspired to keep going, gaining even more momentum to overcome resistance that may have held you back in the past. These concepts may be unlike anything you've worked with before, but remember, genuine transformation comes through upgrading our beliefs, our thoughts, and our behaviours.

SELF-MASTERY & SELF-SABOTAGE

Self-mastery and attainment of optimal health go hand in hand. The prompts and questions throughout this journal will not only guide you in becoming more positive they will also help you to recognise your fears, limiting beliefs and unconscious patterns that limit your ability to achieve your goals.

These unconscious beliefs and behaviours lie hidden in our subconscious, and until we consciously work with them and acknowledge how they run and direct our life, they will continually pop up and sabotage our best intentions.

We need persistent and committed effort to recognise the triggers and behaviours that no longer serve us and actively work on upgrading them to behaviours that move us closer to our goals.

Working with your wellness journal daily will open you up in ways that may sometimes feel wonderful, and at other times may make you feel uncomfortable and even a little emotional. Just know that this is normal. As we confront our fears, our unconscious habits often rise to the surface to be dealt with before we can let them go. While it can be unsettling, it is also a great gift. Thank your old habits for the incredible lessons they offer you, and keep moving courageously forward by choosing new, healthy habits that serve your new healthy lifestyle.

FALLING OFF THE WAGON

It's easy to start strong on a new adventure, but harder to stay inspired after the initial excitement has worn away. You'll probably hit a few dips and bumps, miss a few workouts, skip a few pages of the journal and maybe even have a blowout and eat some junk food along the way. If you do, don't worry. It's okay! This is not about being perfect, it's about being conscious of the choices you make and why you make them. Simply acknowledge any issues that come up and ask yourself a few enlightening questions to gain clarity and get yourself back on track, such as:

WHAT TRIGGERED ME TO SKIP MY TRAINING SESSION?
WHAT MADE ME REACH FOR THAT CHOCOLATE/ICE CREAM/CANDY?
AM I STILL INSPIRED BY MY GOALS?
WHAT FEARS ARE HOLDING ME BACK?
WHY AM I PROCRASTINATING?
WHAT AM I CHOOSING TO FOCUS ON?
WHAT DO I NEED TO START OR STOP?
WHAT DON'T I WANT, AND WHAT WOULD I PREFER?
HOW CAN I STAY ON TRACK WITH MY EATING AND TRAINING?

Use your answers to empower yourself to make adjustments to your plans and then recommit to your why and your wellness goal plan.

THE WAY TO WELLNESS...

A powerful morning and evening practice has the potential to create huge shifts in the quality of your days while helping you to make conscious choices throughout the day. The Daily Pages, divided between a morning and evening session, are intended to be short, focused sessions aligning you with your intentions and goals and training your mind to think positive thoughts that lead to positive actions. How you use your journal, or how much time you spend on it each day is entirely up to you. However, I recommend a minimum of 30 minutes for the morning session, plus your daily exercise, and a minimum of 15 minutes for your evening power questions. Though I recommend following this morning and evening framework, you can refer to your journal anytime you need inspiration, a boost to your spirit, or when you want to move into a better emotional state.

IN THE BEGINNING, YOU MAY WANT TO START SLOWLY BY INCORPORATING A NEW STEP EVERY FEW DAYS UNTIL YOU GET USED TO THE ROUTINE OF ALL EIGHT STEPS.

1. MEDITATION & VISUALISATION:

Practising meditation in the morning is a powerful way to connect to your higher-self and open you up to your gifts of intuition and vitality. Meditation quiets the mind through conscious breathing and stillness and allows you to become aware of your thoughts. Since we can only change what we are aware of, meditation is the perfect place to begin when it comes to personal growth. In that relaxed, centred, and present state, you begin to gain awareness of the thought patterns and behaviours that may be holding you back. Begin with just 5, 10 or 15 minutes twice a day and over time; you'll be able to sit for longer periods. If you're new to meditation, a basic meditation technique is outlined in the coming pages. If you've been meditating for a while, then challenge yourself to sit for longer periods.

Once you're done with your morning meditation, tune into your inner vision and intuiton through visualisation. Using your imagination, visualise on the screen of your mind what you wish to create in the area of your health and wellness. See yourself feeling healthy, eating healthy food, training your body and achieving your goals.

2. DAILY WHY:

Each day you will create and write down your Daily Why. Your why is your reason for staying committed to your goal of improved health, wellness and vitality. It should motivate and inspire you to follow through on your daily actions and steer you back on coarse when you lose your way. An example of a Daily Why could be, "To have an abundance of energy to play with my kids", "To look and feel amazing on my wedding day" or "To have the energy to achieve my career goals".

3. MORNING MINDFULNESS:

Making healthy choices comes down to how positive you feel about yourself. Starting your day with a Morning Mindfulness question makes you feel great and when you feel great, you make great choices. Beginning your day in a peak state is a powerful way to open you up to all the possibilities available to you. Follow the morning prompt and write down your gratitude list, your intentions, your goals, and your purpose for the day. It may be as simple as the healthy food in your fridge, the warm sun on your skin, or a relationship you treasure. Be grateful for things that are still coming, like new possibilities, achieving your goals, and improving your energy. Whatever you focus on, you will attract more of.

4. MORNING MANTRA:

A mantra is an intention that sets your focus, and mindset on what you intend to be, do, or have, at any given moment. Intention is your underlying motivation for all your actions and more than anything else, is responsible for the results you get in life. Consciously choosing your intentions each day, directs your focus and energy to stay centred, no matter what is happening around you. By taking responsibility for your own energy and consciously choosing your emotional state, you can then respond to the world around you instead of unconsciously reacting to it. A mantra can be a word, a personal value, or an affirmation starting with 'I AM' that reminds and guides you towards your highest truth. It's important to feel the intention of your mantra throughout your body, as you say it aloud. This will anchor the energy of your intention into your body's cellular memory. Stating your intentions in this way creates a powerful platform from which to launch your day from.

5. CONSCIOUS EATING:

You know the saying: You are what you eat. Conscious eating is simply being aware of the food that is nourishing and beneficial to your body and focusing on eating only those foods. The food you choose to eat is the fuel that moves your body. Half of your results over the next year will come from the food you choose to eat. You need to eat healthy foods to fuel your active lifestyle, to train your body and to think positive thoughts. When you choose the right foods for your body you can focus better and you're more able to maximise your results. Poor food choices weigh you down, affect your mood and sleep patterns negatively, leaving you unmotivated, depressed and in the worst case, create disease in your body.

If you really want to hit your wellness goals, you need to focus on your diet. Follow the suggestions in the introduction pages but be sure to follow your own intuition for what is right for your body type. For most people though, a diet high in lean protein, fruits, vegetables, whole grains and healthy fats is the foundation for achieving weight loss, building muscle, high energy, good recovery after a workout and a balanced blood sugar level. It's important not to skip meals. Don't believe that starving yourself is the way to lose weight.

Your goal with this step is to eat five to six small portions of high protein meals every three hours and log each meal on your Daily Food Journal. Planning is key. Write your shopping list and plan your meals every Sunday with the Weekly Planner. Each morning prepare your meals for the day and stick to your plan.

6. WORKOUTS:

Energy is your most valuable resource because, when you have the energy you're able to see all the possibilities available to you. Working out daily is essential for creating energy in your body. Be sure to include in your daily routine high intensity training, stretching, yoga, running, or any kind of workout you enjoy. The power of a workout can not be understated. Even when you feel tired, the best pick-me-up is to do a workout. Even if it's just 15 minutes, you'll notice your mood and mindset instantly improve, you're more likely to choose healthier foods, take action on your goals and sleep better at night. The better your physiology, the better your psychology. The combination of positive thoughts, daily workouts and a nutritious diet is the foundation for achieving optimal health.

7. HEALTHY HABITS:

Big changes happen when we take small actions consistently over time. Creating new healthy habits is simply a matter of recognition and repetition until they become part of your lifestyle. As part of your Daily Pages and Weekly Check-in, you will be promoted to focus on creating healthy habits such as staying hydrated and daily stretching. Each day spend time actively thinking about what habits are serving you and then use the reminders, tools and prompts to help reinforce the habits that move you closer to your goals.

8. EVENING REFLECTION:

Each evening you'll have an opportunity to debrief and evaluate your day with the evening reflection question. These prompts are designed to help you review your day and become more self-aware of your choices and behaviours. Spend 15 or 20 minutes before bed to contemplate and answer your evening question. Over time notice how this simple practice not only empowers you to make more conscious choices throughout your day but clears your mind for a good night sleep.

REVIEWS AND PLANNERS

The check-ins, reviews and planners throughout this journal are designed to highlight areas that need your attention while supporting you in upgrading those areas with newly empowered thoughts, habits and actions.

Every Sunday, during your Weekly Check-In, you'll have the opportunity to look back over your past week, to review what is and isn't working and gain clarity on your progress.

You will also have an opportunity to plan your meals, workouts and focus for the coming week using the Weekly Planner. You'll be reminded to review your Wellness Goal Planner, Your Why Statement, to keep yourself motivated and moving towards your goals.

Every quarter, you'll check in with your 90 Day Review to follow up on your progress and celebrate your successes. You'll be prompted to ask yourself a series of questions designed to help you notice your achievements, identify areas you would like to improve, find ways to bring your health back into balance.

After reviewing the previous month, and pulling into focus your most important goals, you'll plan the next quarter using the 90 Day Planner.

At the end of the year, you will complete your Yearly Review, giving you a chance to reflect back on, and celebrate your achievements, learn from your challenges, and consolidate your progress, before launching into another year of wellness.

BASIC MEDITATION TECHNIQUE

WELCOME TO THE BASIC MEDITATION TECHNIQUE. THROUGHOUT THE NEXT YEAR YOU ARE ENCOURAGED TO SPEND TIME MEDITATING AS PART OF YOUR DAILY PRACTICE. FOR SOME OF YOU THIS WILL BE COMPLETELY NEW, WHILE FOR OTHERS IT WILL BE NATURAL AND SIMPLY AN EXTENSION TO YOUR CURRENT DAILY PRACTICE.

The cause of most people's challenges with meditation is believing that it should be hard or somehow difficult. Meditation is nothing more than sitting in stillness with the intention to become conscious of your thoughts. The more you practice sitting in stillness, the more focused you'll be in everyday life. As you create space in your thoughts, you allow new inspiration to enter. As you raise your vibration, you're able to think more clearing and access more of your creative genius. At the highest level, meditation is the path to self-realisation and discovering the source of your true Self - so it's a practice worth practising!

Your goal is to start with just 5 minutes per day and increase your time to at least 25 minutes. At the 25 minute mark, something magical happens that's worth experiencing. As you become more comfortable sitting for longer periods you might like to try sitting for 45 minutes,or even up to 2 hours or more.

To get started, find yourself a comfortable sitting position. You may prefer to sit upright in a chair or cross-legged on the floor. It's not recommended to lie down as while you will want to be completely relaxed, you also want to stay alert. Gently close your eyes and begin to focus on your breath. As you inhale and exhale, bring your focus to the rise and fall of your belly and your breath inhaling and exhale through the tip of your nose. You can also place your focus on the space between your eyes known as your third eye. Placing your awareness here helps draw your energy upwards to create a feeling of lightness and spaciousness.

After some time, you'll notice thoughts arising in your mind, this is completely normal. Simply notice your thoughts without getting drawn into them. Think of your thoughts as holding heavy shopping bags and with your out breath put them down beside you and feel the release of letting them go. Every time you notice a thought arising, use a visualisation technique to simply place that thought down and continue to relax. You can always come back to that thought later - but right now you have no other goal than to be in complete stillness with no thought.

Another analogy is to think of your thoughts as clouds, as they float into your mind, just let them drift right on by and

WITH EACH NEW BREATH, YOUR MIND WILL BECOME CLEARER AND CLEARER.

keep letting go. Notice them but don't attach to them. Keep the blue sky in your mind free from clouds.
As you place down each thought, or you let each thought drift by, whichever best works for you, begin to notice the space opening up in your mind. If your mind wanders, it's ok, simply notice when you get lost in thought and come back to your center and the clear space of no thought. With each new breath, your mind will become clearer and clearer.

Continue to focus on your breath, and soon the quiet space in between your thoughts will become longer and longer.

As you practice this technique, you will naturally be able to meditate for longer periods of time, so start with just 5, 10 or 15 minutes once or twice a day. Once when you wake up and once before bed and over time aim to sit for 25-35 minutes by the end of the journal.

ENJOY YOUR MEDITATION AND PREPARE FOR TRANSFORMATION.

WELCOME TO YOUR WELLNESS FOOD GUIDE

YOU MIGHT BE SURPRISED TO KNOW THAT WHILE YOUR WORKOUTS ARE SUPER IMPORTANT -- THE BIGGEST RESULTS FOR A HEALTHY BODY, MIND AND SPIRIT, COME THROUGH PURIFYING YOUR DIET. THAT MEANS MAKING SMARTER FOOD CHOICES AND SEEING FOOD AS FUEL FOR YOUR BODY.

Optimal health and maintaining a healthy weight is the result of mastering your metabolism. Metabolism establishes the rate at which you burn calories and ultimately how quickly you gain or lose weight.

There are parts to your metabolism you can control and others you can't, like age, gender or genetics. One thing you can control is the food you eat. Poor Fuel In = Poor Energy Out. Good Fuel In = Good Energy Out.

01 EATING CLEAN
Focus on fresh and avoid anything that comes in a can

02 EATING OFTEN
5-6 small high protein meals per day

03 FOCUSING ON HIGH PROTEIN MEALS
Include protein with every meal

04 EXERCISE
Commit to 3-4 high intensity workouts per week

05 DESTRESS
Find ways to reduce unnecessary extra stress on the body

06 SLEEP
Plan to go to bed early and get 7-8 hours per night

07 HYDRATION
Focus on high water intake to energise your active life

FOLLOW THESE 7 STEPS FOR OPTIMAL HEALTH, WELLNESS & VITALITY

WHAT FOODS TO FOCUS ON FOR YOUR SPECIFIC GOALS

THE GOAL:

WEIGHT LOSS

The best way to maintain or reach an ideal weight is to burn more calories than you take in. That means increasing activity and decreasing calorie intake -- but not too much! The safest, most effective diet for weight loss is a healthful, balanced one including:

01. Cutting junk food, sugary sodas, and sweet, undiluted fruit drinks out of your diet is an easy way to lose weight over time. Portion control is also important when you're trying to lose weight.

02. Don't skip meals to "save" calories. You'll likely make up for the skipped meals by snacking later on junk foods, which are high in calories, sugar, and trans fats.

03. Eat more lean protein to control your appetite. Go for low-fat dairy, skinless chicken and turkey, fish, lean cuts of beef, pork, and veal and nuts and seeds. Avoid animal foods that are high in saturated fats.

04. Eat more vegetables, fruits, whole grains, and beans. Plant-based foods are high in water and fiber with essential vitamins and antioxidants, yet very low in calories.

THE GOAL:

BUILDING MUSCLE

If you want to add lean muscle you need to add sufficient calories and protein to your diet along with proper strength training to ensure you gain weight in all the right places. You should not bulk up from resistance training. However, if you start getting bigger, it is most likely because you're eating more. This isn't a problem -- as adding a little more lean mass is a good thing and it increases your metabolism so you burn more fat.

To build muscle, focus on eating protein-rich snacks such as high-protein energy bars or a protein shake immediately after training to give your muscles the necessary post-workout fuel. Apart from your four other high protein meals during the day, eating a high-protein snack before bedtime also helps to build muscle even while you sleeep. Sounds good!

THE GOAL:

WEIGHT GAIN

When it comes to gaining weight, calories count, but so do nutrients! Gaining weight requires eating calorie-rich but also nutrient-rich foods -- not just high-calorie foods with lots of fat, sugar, or empty calories.

The goal is to choose foods that are packed with vitamins, minerals, nutrients, and calories so each bite is loaded with good nutrition. A good idea is to add some extra olive oil, nuts and full fat yoghurt to your diet, for example. Also you need to eat often - eating meals or mini-meals more often is the best way to pack more calories into your day.

THE GOAL:

MORE ENERGY/ ENDURANCE

If you want more energy, you need to eat more often, ideally every 3-4 hours, as this will keep your energy levels and blood sugar up and more consistent throughout the day. Eating high protein meals with a good balance of fresh fruit and vegetables should give you the energy you need to sustain you throughout the day. If you're still struggling -- try a good multi-vitamin that can assist you.

Reaching for a healthy snack like an apple, nuts, or a handful of baby carrots is a great way to refuel if you're running low on energy. Nutrition bars can be convenient, but they are often high in sugar so be sure to read the label. And finally, drink plenty of water. most people don't drink enough to balance the loss from sweating from physical activity. Staying well hydrated will really help with consistent energy throughout the day.

MOST PEOPLE FEEL MORE ENERGETIC THROUGHOUT THE DAY AFTER EXERCISE

7 SIMPLE DIET TIPS FOR MAXIMIZING RESULTS

DRINK LOTS OF WATER!

Most of us are hugely dehydrated and holding fluids due to not drinking enough. If you do NOTHING ELSE -- start drinking 8 glasses of water every single day.

THE BENEFITS

faster recovery
more energy
flushing toxins
alleviates fluid
and bloating

tones, tightens and
helps you shed weight
gives you glowing skin

EAT A HIGH PROTEIN MEAL WITHIN 30 MINS OF WAKING UP OR FOR BREAKFAST

Here are some ideas: boiled, fried or scrambled eggs, spinach, protein shake/smoothie

THE BENEFITS

lose excess belly fat
more energy
throughout the day

kick starts your
metabolism

FOCUS ON EATING FIVE SMALL MEALS PER DAY EVERY 3 HOURS INSTEAD OF THREE BIG MEALS.

By eating smaller meals more often it boosts your metabolism and ensures your body doesn't go into starvation mode and start storing fat.

THE BENEFITS

- consistent energy
- boosts metabolism
- feeds muscle growth
- less likely to make poor food choices
- never hungry

UP YOUR VEGGIE INTAKE!

Basically veggie's RULE and you need to add them to as many meals as possible. Learn to LOVE greens like broccoli, spinach, zucchini, lettuce, and the reds and yellows like tomatoes, peppers and squash. Try to eat leafy greens with at least two of your meals every day. If that's too hard, just start with at one meal.

THE BENEFITS

- high in nutrients
- boosts your metabolism
- feeds muscle growth
- satisfying hunger
- increases your stamina

HIGH PROTEIN MEALS SHOULD BE ONE OF YOUR PRIMARY FOCUSES WITH EVERY MEAL.

Protein can come in many forms such as meat, tofu, tempeh, fish, protein powders, vegetables, nuts, lentils, beans and diary products like cottage cheese & greek yoghurts.

THE BENEFITS

- high in protein
- boosts metabolism
- builds lean muscle
- increases stamina
- decreases hunger

FOCUS ON BRINGING YOUR BODY INTO AN ALKALINE STATE.

Most disease, stress and illness is caused by the body being too acidic. A balanced alkaline body is a healthy body. To balance your PH, focus on alkaline foods.

THE BENEFITS

- balances your body's natural PH levels
- boosts metabolism
- reduces free radicals
- overall wellbeing

ACIDIC FOODS

Coffee	White	Shrimp	Mustard
Black Tea	Breads	Tuna	Pepper
Sauces	Pasta &	Turkey	Soft Drinks
Wine	Rice	Butter	Vinegar
Sugar	Beef	Beer	Garlic
Refined	Fish	Hard Liquor	
Carbs	Lamb	Spirits	
Milk	Lobster	Cocoa	

ALKALINE FOODS

Alfalfa	Spinach	Lemon	Cinnamon
Greens	Spirulina	Lime	Ginger
Beetroot	Sprouts	Raspberries	Miso
Broccoli	Sweet	Rhubarb	Sea Salt
Cabbage	Potatoes	Strawberries	
Carrot	Apple	Tomato	
Cauliflower	Apricot	Watermelon	
Celery	Avocado	Almonds	
Green	Banana	Tempeh	
Beans	Blackberries	Tofu	
Lettuce	Coconut	Whey	
Mushrooms	Grapes	Protein	
Pumpkin	Grapefruit	Powder	

REPEAT AFTER ME: FATS ARE GOOD, SUGARS ARE EVIL!

Yes, that's right. You actually need good fats to have a heathy and fit body. Fats can actually help you lose wight and tone up. If you have a choice between eating something high in fat verses high in sugar -- always take the fat option. But we don't mean fried fats -- we mean GOOD fats.

So what are good fats? Things like: Olive Oil, Avocado, Coconut Oil, Nuts, Seeds, Flax Seed Oil

THE BENEFITS

- boosts metabolism
- burns fat
- promotes muscle growth

MEAL PLANNER INSPIRATION

ROCK YOUR WEEKLY MEALS USING OUR MEAL PLANNER. TRY THESE SUGGESTIONS OR SIMPLY USE THEM AS INSPIRATION TO KEEP YOUR MEALS INTERESTING AND FUN!

	MONDAY	TUESDAY	WEDNESDAY
(Meal 01) **BREAKFAST**	Fresh Berries & Greek Yoghurt	Oatmeal with Almond Milk	Eggs, Spinach & Mushrooms
(Meal 02) **SNACK**	Celery & Peanut Butter	Cottage Cheese/ Apple/Walnuts/ Cinnamon	Green Smoothie -- design your own or see recipe
(Meal 03) **LUNCH**	Steamed Asian Vegetables	Greek Salad w Chicken or your favorite protein	Fresh Beetroot, Pine nuts, Spinach & Feta Salad
(Meal 04) **SNACK**	Nut Mix	Baked Sweet Potato	Greek Yoghurt
(Meal 05) **DINNER**	Salmon & Steamed Broccoli	Grilled Chicken & Couscous	Vegetable Stir-fry with Brown Rice
(Meal 06) **DESSERT**	Frozen Berries	1-2 Dark Chocolate Pieces	Fresh Strawberries

THURSDAY	FRIDAY	SATURDAY	SUNDAY
Breakfast Smoothie - Banana, Cinnamon, ...	Omelette & Wholegrain Toast	Poached Eggs & Avocado	Protein Pancakes
Greek Yoghurt & Fruit Parfait	Carrot Sticks & Low Fat Tzatziki	Pink Grapefruit	Kiwi, Apple, Cottage Cheese & Almonds
Tuna, Egg & Green Bean Salad	3 Bean Salad	Quinoa, Feta, Spinach Salad	Bean Tacos with Fresh Salad
Cold Lentil Soup	Celery & Low Fat Hummus	Frozen Berries & Cottage Cheese	Cucumber Sticks with Peanut butter
Whole Wheat Vegetable Pasta w Homemade Pasta Sauce	Tofu & Stir-Fried Vegetables	Vietnamese Rice Paper Rolls with Tuna and Salad	Roast Vegetable with meat/ chicken/ fish
Natural Frozen Yoghurt (low sugar)	Fresh Blueberries	Pineapple & Passionfruit Parfait	Apple, Cinnamon & Greek Yoghurt

What is my definition of health and wellness?

....
....

Does my current lifestyle help or hinder my health and wellness?
What is one action I can do to improve that?

....
....

Is the work I am doing fulfilling and does it benefit health and wellness?

....
....

How would improving my health and wellness, improve my relationship with my family?

....
....

What fears do I have about becoming more fit? What do I fear will change?

....
....

What beliefs do I hold that prevent me from having the health/fitness/body I want?

....
....

What baggage am I holding on to that keeps me stuck in self-sabotaging behaviour?

....
....

Do I believe I deserve unlimited health and wellness?

....
....

What are my partner's goals for health and wellness and how do those help or hinder my goals?

....
....

What is my current relationship to food and how can I improve it?

....
....

Would my family describe me as generally healthy or unhealthy?
What would I need to do to change that?

....
....

What circumstances or excuses stop me from having an active and healthy lifestyle?

....
....

How can I surround myself with people who inspire a healthy lifestyle?

....

....

What new hobbies, sports or activities can I start to improve my healthy lifestyle?

....

....

Who do I need to set healthy boundaries with to improve my overall wellbeing?

....

....

How can we have more fun as a family and be active, fit and healthy at the same time?

....

....

What new mindset do I want to adopt into my life around health and wellness and why?

....

....

How can I be an example of health and wellness for my family?

....

....

How can I be more knowledgeable about health related issues that can serve me?

....

....

Do I have healthy fun or it is destructive? What could I do differently to improve my health?

....

....

Who are my professional advisors and practitioners when it comes to my health and wellness? Who would I love on my team?

....

....

How is my current attitude and mindset towards the concept of health and wellness? What would I like my mindset to be?

....

....

What are my most important goals around health and wellness that I want to achieve?

....

....

What big hearth and wellness goal will I set for myself over the next 12 months?

....

....

MY WHY STATEMENT

Your Why Statement is a clear, concise statement summing up the reason and purpose behind wanting to achieve your wellness goals. Your why should inspire and motivate you to reach for your potential, and is the driving force behind all your choices, intentions and actions each day.

Here are a few questions to help uncover your why:

Why is health and wellness important to me?
What do I love to do and how does my health affect my ability to do more of this?
What gifts and talents do I wish to share with the world?
What does the concept of optimal health, wellness and vitality mean to me?

Take some time to craft your Why Statement below:

	One Massive Action...	Where I want to be...	Where I am now...
Health & Body			
Emotional, Spiritual & Personal Growth			
Intimate Relationship			
Social & Fun			
Family & Friends			
Work & Career			
Money & Finances			
Community & Giving			

WELLNESS GOAL PLANNER

	WHAT is my specific goal and what do I want in this area of my life? What would I love to HAVE?	WHY do I want it? What is my purpose for achieving this goal? How will this goal benefit my life or how will it affect my life, if I don't achieve it?
Health & Body		
Emotional, Spiritual & Personal Growth		
Intimate Relationship		
Friends & Family		
Social & Fun		
Work & Career		
Money & Finances		
Community & Giving		

WHO do I need to BE to achieve this goal? What mindset do I need to aquire to succeed?

What is my specific PLAN and what do I need to DO to achieve this goal?

YEARLY PLANNER

JANUARY >
week

1

2

3

4

FEBRUARY >
week

1

2

3

4

MARCH >
week

1

2

3

4

APRIL >
week

1

2

3

4

MAY >
week

1

2

3

4

JUNE >
week

1

2

3

4

JULY >

week

1

2

3

4

OCTOBER >

week

1

2

3

4

AUGUST >

week

1

2

3

4

NOVEMBER >

week

1

2

3

4

SEPTEMBER >

week

1

2

3

4

DECEMBER >

week

1

2

3

4

- [ ] Meditation
- [ ] 8 Glasses of water
- [ ] Visualisation
- [ ] Stretching

DAILY WHY

DATE

Today would be amazing if:

Today, I practised mindfulness when:

Breakfast

Snack am

Lunch

Snack pm

Dinner

WORKOUT

Today's wellness mantra

HEALTH HABITS

☐ Meditation ☐ 8 Glasses of water

☐ Visualisation ☐ Stretching

Today, I'm open to the possibility of:

When did I show willpower today?

WORKOUT

Breakfast

Snack am

Lunch

Today's wellness mantra

Snack pm

Dinner

☐ Meditation   ☐ 8 Glasses of water

☐ Visualisation ☐ Stretching

Today, I'm going to focus on eating:

What went well today?

Breakfast

Snack am

Lunch

Snack pm

Dinner

WORKOUT

....

....

Today's wellness mantra

WEEKLY CHECK-IN

What progress have I made this week?

☐ Review My Wellness
Goal Planner

☐ Review My Why Statement

☐ Complete My Weekly Planner

What's working and why is it working?

What's not working and what am I willing to do about it?

What steps can I take to focus my diet on eating more fresh and healthy foods?

What is one thing I can do every day to take care of my body?

What three things do I most enjoy by improving my health?

What is one thing I can do this week that will create the biggest results for my health & wellness?

OLD HABIT >	NEW HABIT >	NEW ACTIONS >	NEW AFFIRMATION / MANTRA

WEEKLY PLANNER

Shopping list:

NEW HEALTHY HABIT FOCUS

	BREAKFAST SNACK / WORKOUTS / CLASSES	LUNCH SNACK / WORKOUTS / CLASSES	DINNER SNACK / WORKOUTS / CLASSES
MONDAY			
TUESDAY			
WEDNESDAY			
THURSDAY			
FRIDAY			
SATURDAY			
SUNDAY			

DATE

DAILY WHY

HEALTH HABITS

☐ Meditation   ☐ 8 Glasses of water

☐ Visualisation   ☐ Stretching

Today, I'm grateful for:

How did I feel in my body today and why?

WORKOUT

....

....

Today's wellness mantra

Breakfast

Snack am

Lunch

Snack pm

Dinner

HEALTH HABITS

- [ ] Meditation
- [ ] 8 Glasses of water
- [ ] Visualisation
- [ ] Stretching

DAILY WHY

DATE

My intention for today is:

What habits do I most want to improve and why?

Breakfast

Snack am

Lunch

Snack pm

Dinner

WORKOUT

....

....

Today's wellness mantra

DATE

HEALTH HABITS

☐ Meditation ☐ 8 Glasses of water

☐ Visualisation ☐ Stretching

What I love about my body is:

In what way did I practice conscious eating today?

WORKOUT

....

....

Today's wellness mantra

Breakfast

Snack am

Lunch

Snack pm

Dinner

HEALTH HABITS

- [ ] Meditation
- [ ] Visualisation
- [ ] 8 Glasses of water
- [ ] Stretching

DAILY WHY

DATE

Today is my opportunity to:

What did I notice about my mindset today?

Breakfast

Snack am

Lunch

Snack pm

Dinner

WORKOUT

....

....

Today's wellness mantra

DATE

DAILY WHY

HEALTH HABITS

☐ Meditation   ☐ 8 Glasses of water

☐ Visualisation   ☐ Stretching

Today is going to be great because:

What was today's lesson?

WORKOUT

....

....

Today's wellness mantra

Breakfast

Snack am

Lunch

Snack pm

Dinner

HEALTH HABITS

☐ Meditation ☐ 8 Glasses of water

☐ Visualisation ☐ Stretching

DAILY WHY

DATE

Today, I'm excited to create:

How did I show discipline and move closer to my wellness goals today?

Breakfast

Snack am

Lunch

Snack pm

Dinner

WORKOUT

....

....

Today's wellness mantra

DATE

WEEKLY CHECK-IN

My week in review

What goals have I achieved this week?

☐ Review My Wellness Goal Planner

☐ Review My Why Statement

☐ Complete My Weekly Planner

What's going well and why is it?

What's most challenging and how can I turn it to my advantage?

How can I drink more water every day?

What do I need to START doing to have better health?

What do I need to STOP doing for better health?

What is one thing I can do this week that will create the biggest results for my health & wellness?

OLD HABIT >	NEW HABIT >	NEW ACTIONS >	NEW AFFIRMATION / MANTRA

WEEKLY PLANNER

Shopping list:

	BREAKFAST SNACK / WORKOUTS / CLASSES	LUNCH SNACK / WORKOUTS / CLASSES	DINNER SNACK / WORKOUTS / CLASSES
MONDAY			
TUESDAY			
WEDNESDAY			
THURSDAY			
FRIDAY			
SATURDAY			
SUNDAY			

DATE

HEALTH HABITS

☐ Meditation   ☐ 8 Glasses of water

☐ Visualisation   ☐ Stretching

Today, I'm going to focus on being:

What strengths did I use today?

WORKOUT

Breakfast

Snack am

Lunch

Today's wellness mantra

Snack pm

Dinner

HEALTH HABITS

☐ Meditation   ☐ 8 Glasses of water

☐ Visualisation   ☐ Stretching

DAILY WHY

DATE

Today would be amazing if:

Today, I practised mindfulness when:

Breakfast

Snack am

Lunch

Snack pm

Dinner

WORKOUT

....

....

Today's wellness mantra

HEALTH HABITS

☐ Meditation ☐ 8 Glasses of water

☐ Visualisation ☐ Stretching

Today, I'm open to the possibility of:

When did I show willpower today?

WORKOUT

....

....

Today's wellness mantra

Breakfast

Snack am

Lunch

Snack pm

Dinner

- [ ] Meditation
- [ ] 8 Glasses of water
- [ ] Visualisation
- [ ] Stretching

DATE

Today, I'm going to focus on eating:

What went well today?

Breakfast

Snack am

Lunch

Snack pm

Dinner

WORKOUT

....

....

Today's wellness mantra

Meditation ☐   8 Glasses of water ☐

Visualisation ☐   Stretching ☐

Today, I'm grateful for:

How did I feel in my body today and why?

WORKOUT

....

....

Today's wellness mantra

Breakfast

Snack am

Lunch

Snack pm

Dinner

- [ ] Meditation
- [ ] 8 Glasses of water
- [ ] Visualisation
- [ ] Stretching

My intention for today is:

What habits do I most want to improve and why?

Breakfast

Snack am

Lunch

Snack pm

Dinner

WORKOUT

Today's wellness mantra

WEEKLY CHECK-IN

What progress have I made this week?

☐ Review My Wellness
   Goal Planner

☐ Review My Why Statement

☐ Complete My Weekly Planner

Where do I see results & why?

What do I need to start or stop?

When do I feel the best in my body and mind?

What does my body need most, right now?

When and how do I sabotage my health and wellness goals?

What is one thing I can do this week that will create the biggest results for my health & wellness?

OLD HABIT >	NEW HABIT >	NEW ACTIONS >	NEW AFFIRMATION / MANTRA

WEEKLY PLANNER

Shopping list:

	BREAKFAST SNACK / WORKOUTS / CLASSES	LUNCH SNACK / WORKOUTS / CLASSES	DINNER SNACK / WORKOUTS / CLASSES
MONDAY			
TUESDAY			
WEDNESDAY			
THURSDAY			
FRIDAY			
SATURDAY			
SUNDAY			

DATE	DAILY WHY	HEALTH HABITS

HEALTH HABITS

☐ Meditation   ☐ 8 Glasses of water

☐ Visualisation   ☐ Stretching

What I love about my body is:

In what way did I practice conscious eating today?

WORKOUT

....

....

Today's wellness mantra

Breakfast

Snack am

Lunch

Snack pm

Dinner

☐ Meditation   ☐ 8 Glasses of water

☐ Visualisation   ☐ Stretching

DAILY WHY

DATE

Today is my opportunity to:

What did I notice about my mindset today?

Breakfast

Snack am

Lunch

Snack pm

Dinner

WORKOUT

Today's wellness mantra

DATE

HEALTH HABITS

☐ Meditation   ☐ 8 Glasses of water

☐ Visualisation   ☐ Stretching

Today is going to be great because:

What was today's lesson?

WORKOUT

Breakfast

Snack am

Lunch

Snack pm

Today's wellness mantra

Dinner

- [ ] Meditation
- [ ] 8 Glasses of water
- [ ] Visualisation
- [ ] Stretching

DAILY WHY

DATE

Today, I'm excited to create:

How did I show discipline and move closer to my wellness goals today?

Breakfast

Snack am

Lunch

Snack pm

Dinner

WORKOUT

Today's wellness mantra

DATE

HEALTH HABITS

☐ Meditation   ☐ 8 Glasses of water

☐ Visualisation   ☐ Stretching

Today, I'm going to focus on being:

What strengths did I use today?

WORKOUT

Breakfast

Snack am

Lunch

Snack pm

Today's wellness mantra

Dinner

☐ Meditation   ☐ 8 Glasses of water

☐ Visualisation   ☐ Stretching

Today would be amazing if:

Today, I practised mindfulness when:

Breakfast

Snack am

Lunch

Snack pm

Dinner

WORKOUT

Today's wellness mantra

WEEKLY CHECK-IN

My week in review

What major goals have I achieved this month?

☐ Review My Wellness Goal Planner

☐ Review My Why Statement

☐ Complete My Weekly Planner

Where am I having success and why?

What are the biggest distractions to improving my health and how can I remove them?

What does my body tell me I need to eat more or less of?

Do I eat too much or too little for a strong, healthy body?

What am I enjoying most about my journey to better health?

What is one thing I can do this week that will create the biggest results for my health & wellness?

OLD HABIT >	NEW HABIT >	NEW ACTIONS >	NEW AFFIRMATION / MANTRA

WEEKLY PLANNER

Shopping list:

NEW HEALTHY HABIT FOCUS

	BREAKFAST SNACK / WORKOUTS / CLASSES	LUNCH SNACK / WORKOUTS / CLASSES	DINNER SNACK / WORKOUTS / CLASSES
MONDAY			
TUESDAY			
WEDNESDAY			
THURSDAY			
FRIDAY			
SATURDAY			
SUNDAY			

☐ Meditation   ☐ 8 Glasses of water

☐ Visualisation   ☐ Stretching

Today, I'm open to the possibility of:

When did I show willpower today?

WORKOUT

Breakfast

Snack am

Lunch

Snack pm

Today's wellness mantra

Dinner

HEALTH HABITS

☐ Meditation   ☐ 8 Glasses of water

☐ Visualisation   ☐ Stretching

DAILY WHY

DATE

Today, I'm going to focus on eating:

What went well today?

Breakfast

Snack am

Lunch

Snack pm

Dinner

WORKOUT

Today's wellness mantra

DATE

DAILY WHY

HEALTH HABITS

☐ Meditation   ☐ 8 Glasses of water

☐ Visualisation   ☐ Stretching

Today, I'm grateful for:

How did I feel in my body today and why?

WORKOUT

....

....

Today's wellness mantra

Breakfast

Snack am

Lunch

Snack pm

Dinner

HEALTH HABITS

- [ ] Meditation
- [ ] 8 Glasses of water
- [ ] Visualisation
- [ ] Stretching

DAILY WHY

DATE

My intention for today is:

What habits do I most want to improve and why?

Breakfast

Snack am

Lunch

Snack pm

Dinner

WORKOUT

....

....

Today's wellness mantra

DATE

HEALTH HABITS

☐ Meditation ☐ 8 Glasses of water

☐ Visualisation ☐ Stretching

What I love about my body is:

In what way did I practice conscious eating today?

WORKOUT

Breakfast

Snack am

Lunch

Snack pm

Today's wellness mantra

Dinner

☐ Meditation   ☐ 8 Glasses of water

☐ Visualisation   ☐ Stretching

DAILY WHY

DATE

Today is my opportunity to:

What did I notice about my mindset today?

Breakfast

Snack am

Lunch

Snack pm

Dinner

WORKOUT

Today's wellness mantra

WEEKLY CHECK-IN

What progress have I made this week?

☐ Review My Wellness Goal Planner

☐ Review My Why Statement

☐ Complete My Weekly Planner

What's working and why is it working?

What's not working and what am I willing to do about it?

What steps can I take to focus my diet on eating more fresh and healthy foods?

What is one thing I can do every day to take care of my body?

What three things do I most enjoy by improving my health?

What is one thing I can do this week that will create the biggest results for my health & wellness?

OLD HABIT >	NEW HABIT >	NEW ACTIONS >	NEW AFFIRMATION / MANTRA

WEEKLY PLANNER

Shopping list:

	BREAKFAST SNACK / WORKOUTS / CLASSES	LUNCH SNACK / WORKOUTS / CLASSES	DINNER SNACK / WORKOUTS / CLASSES
MONDAY			
TUESDAY			
WEDNESDAY			
THURSDAY			
FRIDAY			
SATURDAY			
SUNDAY			

DATE

DAILY WHY

HEALTH HABITS

- [ ] Meditation
- [ ] 8 Glasses of water
- [ ] Visualisation
- [ ] Stretching

Today is going to be great because:

What was today's lesson?

WORKOUT

....

....

Today's wellness mantra

Breakfast

Snack am

Lunch

Snack pm

Dinner

- [ ] Meditation
- [ ] 8 Glasses of water
- [ ] Visualisation
- [ ] Stretching

Today, I'm excited to create:

How did I show discipline and move closer to my wellness goals today?

Breakfast

Snack am

Lunch

Snack pm

Dinner

WORKOUT

Today's wellness mantra

DATE	DAILY WHY		HEALTH HABITS

HEALTH HABITS

- [ ] Meditation
- [ ] 8 Glasses of water
- [ ] Visualisation
- [ ] Stretching

Today, I'm going to focus on being:

What strengths did I use today?

WORKOUT

....

....

Today's wellness mantra

Breakfast

Snack am

Lunch

Snack pm

Dinner

HEALTH HABITS

☐ Meditation ☐ 8 Glasses of water

☐ Visualisation ☐ Stretching

DAILY WHY

DATE

Today would be amazing if:

Today, I practised mindfulness when:

Breakfast

Snack am

Lunch

Snack pm

Dinner

WORKOUT

Today's wellness mantra

DATE

DAILY WHY

HEALTH HABITS

☐ Meditation ☐ 8 Glasses of water

☐ Visualisation ☐ Stretching

Today, I'm open to the possibility of:

When did I show willpower today?

WORKOUT

....

....

Today's wellness mantra

Breakfast

Snack am

Lunch

Snack pm

Dinner

HEALTH HABITS

☐ Meditation ☐ 8 Glasses of water

☐ Visualisation ☐ Stretching

DAILY WHY

DATE

Today, I'm going to focus on eating:

What went well today?

Breakfast

Snack am

Lunch

Snack pm

Dinner

WORKOUT

....

....

Today's wellness mantra

WEEKLY CHECK-IN

My week in review

What goals have I achieved this week?

☐ Review My Wellness Goal Planner

☐ Review My Why Statement

☐ Complete My Weekly Planner

What's going well and why is it?

What's most challenging and how can I turn it to my advantage?

How can I drink more water every day?

What do I need to START doing to have better health?

What do I need to STOP doing for better health?

What is one thing I can do this week that will create the biggest results for my health & wellness?

OLD HABIT >	NEW HABIT >	NEW ACTIONS >	NEW AFFIRMATION / MANTRA

WEEKLY PLANNER

Shopping list:

NEW HEALTHY HABIT FOCUS

	BREAKFAST SNACK / WORKOUTS / CLASSES	LUNCH SNACK / WORKOUTS / CLASSES	DINNER SNACK / WORKOUTS / CLASSES
MONDAY			
TUESDAY			
WEDNESDAY			
THURSDAY			
FRIDAY			
SATURDAY			
SUNDAY			

DATE

DAILY WHY

HEALTH HABITS

- [ ] Meditation
- [ ] 8 Glasses of water
- [ ] Visualisation
- [ ] Stretching

Today, I'm grateful for:

How did I feel in my body today and why?

WORKOUT

....

....

Today's wellness mantra

Breakfast

Snack am

Lunch

Snack pm

Dinner

HEALTH HABITS

- [ ] Meditation
- [ ] 8 Glasses of water
- [ ] Visualisation
- [ ] Stretching

DAILY WHY

DATE

My intention for today is:

What habits do I most want to improve and why?

Breakfast

Snack am

Lunch

Snack pm

Dinner

WORKOUT

....

....

Today's wellness mantra

☐ Meditation ☐ 8 Glasses of water

☐ Visualisation ☐ Stretching

What I love about my body is:

In what way did I practice conscious eating today?

WORKOUT

Breakfast

Snack am

Lunch

Today's wellness mantra

Snack pm

Dinner

HEALTH HABITS	DAILY WHY	DATE

☐ Meditation   ☐ 8 Glasses of water

☐ Visualisation   ☐ Stretching

Today is my opportunity to:

What did I notice about my mindset today?

Breakfast

Snack am

Lunch

Snack pm

Dinner

WORKOUT

....

....

Today's wellness mantra

DATE

HEALTH HABITS

- ☐ Meditation
- ☐ 8 Glasses of water
- ☐ Visualisation
- ☐ Stretching

Today is going to be great because:

What was today's lesson?

WORKOUT

....

....

Today's wellness mantra

Breakfast

Snack am

Lunch

Snack pm

Dinner

HEALTH HABITS

- [ ] Meditation
- [ ] 8 Glasses of water
- [ ] Visualisation
- [ ] Stretching

DAILY WHY

DATE

Today, I'm excited to create:

How did I show discipline and move closer to my wellness goals today?

Breakfast

Snack am

Lunch

Snack pm

Dinner

WORKOUT

Today's wellness mantra

WEEKLY CHECK-IN

My week in review

What progress have I made this week?

☐ Review My Wellness Goal Planner

☐ Review My Why Statement

☐ Complete My Weekly Planner

Where do I see results & why?

What do I need to start or stop?

When do I feel the best in my body and mind?

What does my body need most, right now?

When and how do I sabotage my health and wellness goals?

What is one thing I can do this week that will create the biggest results for my health & wellness?

OLD HABIT >	NEW HABIT >	NEW ACTIONS >	NEW AFFIRMATION / MANTRA

WEEKLY PLANNER

Shopping list:

NEW HEALTHY HABIT FOCUS

	BREAKFAST SNACK / WORKOUTS / CLASSES	LUNCH SNACK / WORKOUTS / CLASSES	DINNER SNACK / WORKOUTS / CLASSES
MONDAY			
TUESDAY			
WEDNESDAY			
THURSDAY			
FRIDAY			
SATURDAY			
SUNDAY			

☐ Meditation   ☐ 8 Glasses of water

☐ Visualisation   ☐ Stretching

Today, I'm going to focus on being:

What strengths did I use today?

WORKOUT

....

....

Today's wellness mantra

Breakfast

Snack am

Lunch

Snack pm

Dinner

HEALTH HABITS

☐ Meditation ☐ 8 Glasses of water

☐ Visualisation ☐ Stretching

DAILY WHY

DATE

Today would be amazing if:

Today, I practised mindfulness when:

Breakfast

Snack am

Lunch

Snack pm

Dinner

WORKOUT

Today's wellness mantra

DATE

HEALTH HABITS

☐ Meditation   ☐ 8 Glasses of water

☐ Visualisation   ☐ Stretching

Today, I'm open to the possibility of: When did I show willpower today?

WORKOUT   Breakfast

....

                                                 Snack am

....

                                                 Lunch

                                                 Snack pm

Today's wellness mantra

                                                 Dinner

- [ ] Meditation
- [ ] 8 Glasses of water
- [ ] Visualisation
- [ ] Stretching

DAILY WHY

DATE

Today, I'm going to focus on eating:

What went well today?

Breakfast

Snack am

Lunch

Snack pm

Dinner

WORKOUT

....

....

Today's wellness mantra

☐ Meditation ☐ 8 Glasses of water

☐ Visualisation ☐ Stretching

Today, I'm grateful for:

How did I feel in my body today and why?

WORKOUT

....

....

Today's wellness mantra

Breakfast

Snack am

Lunch

Snack pm

Dinner

HEALTH HABITS

- [ ] Meditation
- [ ] 8 Glasses of water
- [ ] Visualisation
- [ ] Stretching

DAILY WHY

DATE

My intention for today is:

What habits do I most want to improve and why?

Breakfast

Snack am

Lunch

Snack pm

Dinner

WORKOUT

....

....

Today's wellness mantra

WEEKLY CHECK-IN

What major goals have I achieved this month?

☐ Review My Wellness Goal Planner

☐ Review My Why Statement

☐ Complete My Weekly Planner

Where am I having success and why?

What are the biggest distractions to improving my health and how can I remove them?

What does my body tell me I need to eat more or less of?

Do I eat too much or too little for a strong, healthy body?

What am I enjoying most about my journey to better health?

What is one thing I can do this week that will create the biggest results for my health & wellness?

OLD HABIT >	NEW HABIT >	NEW ACTIONS >	NEW AFFIRMATION / MANTRA

WEEKLY PLANNER

Shopping list:

	BREAKFAST SNACK / WORKOUTS / CLASSES	LUNCH SNACK / WORKOUTS / CLASSES	DINNER SNACK / WORKOUTS / CLASSES
MONDAY			
TUESDAY			
WEDNESDAY			
THURSDAY			
FRIDAY			
SATURDAY			
SUNDAY			

- [ ] Meditation
- [ ] 8 Glasses of water
- [ ] Visualisation
- [ ] Stretching

What I love about my body is:

In what way did I practice conscious eating today?

WORKOUT

....

....

Today's wellness mantra

Breakfast

Snack am

Lunch

Snack pm

Dinner

HEALTH HABITS

☐ Meditation ☐ 8 Glasses of water

☐ Visualisation ☐ Stretching

DAILY WHY

DATE

Today is my opportunity to:

What did I notice about my mindset today?

Breakfast

Snack am

Lunch

Snack pm

Dinner

WORKOUT

Today's wellness mantra

DATE

HEALTH HABITS

☐ Meditation   ☐ 8 Glasses of water

☐ Visualisation ☐ Stretching

Today is going to be great because:

What was today's lesson?

WORKOUT

....

....

Today's wellness mantra

Breakfast

Snack am

Lunch

Snack pm

Dinner

- [ ] Meditation
- [ ] 8 Glasses of water
- [ ] Visualisation
- [ ] Stretching

Today, I'm excited to create:

How did I show discipline and move closer to my wellness goals today?

Breakfast

Snack am

Lunch

Snack pm

Dinner

WORKOUT

Today's wellness mantra

DAILY WHY

HEALTH HABITS

☐ Meditation ☐ 8 Glasses of water

☐ Visualisation ☐ Stretching

Today, I'm going to focus on being:

What strengths did I use today?

WORKOUT

Today's wellness mantra

Breakfast

Snack am

Lunch

Snack pm

Dinner

HEALTH HABITS

☐ Meditation ☐ 8 Glasses of water

☐ Visualisation ☐ Stretching

DAILY WHY

DATE

Today would be amazing if:

Today, I practised mindfulness when:

Breakfast

Snack am

Lunch

Snack pm

Dinner

WORKOUT

....

....

Today's wellness mantra

90 DAY REVIEW

What goals have I completed this past 90 days that have improved my health and wellness? How do I feel?

What's going well and why?
What mindset changes do I wish to make around my health and wellness?
What is no longer acceptable to me?

What do I need to STOP doing?

What do I need to START doing?

What limiting beliefs are holding me back from personal growth and better wellbeing?

What decisions do I need to make that I have been putting off around my health?

What activities do I spend my time on and how do they contribute to my health and wellness?

What new health goal am I focusing on for the next 90 days?
What would I love to achieve?

- [ ] Review My Wellness Goal Planner
- [ ] Review My Why Statement
- [ ] Check My Healthy Habits
- [ ] Complete My 90 Day Planner
- [ ] Plan My Week
- [ ] Celebrate My Progress!

90 DAY PLANNER

Goal:

Target date:

Actions to complete this goal:

WHY I'D LOVE TO ACHIEVE THIS GOAL:

HOW WILL I FEEL WHEN I'VE REACHED THIS GOAL?

Goal:

Target date:

Actions to complete this goal:

WHY I'D LOVE TO ACHIEVE THIS GOAL:

HOW WILL I FEEL WHEN I'VE REACHED THIS GOAL?

Goal:

Target date:

Actions to complete this goal:

WHY I'D LOVE TO ACHIEVE THIS GOAL:

HOW WILL I FEEL WHEN I'VE REACHED THIS GOAL?

Goal:

Target date:

Actions to complete this goal:

WHY I'D LOVE TO ACHIEVE THIS GOAL:

HOW WILL I FEEL WHEN I'VE REACHED THIS GOAL?

A HEALTHY OUTSIDE STARTS ON THE INSIDE.

WEEKLY PLANNER

Shopping list:

	BREAKFAST SNACK / WORKOUTS / CLASSES	LUNCH SNACK / WORKOUTS / CLASSES	DINNER SNACK / WORKOUTS / CLASSES
MONDAY			
TUESDAY			
WEDNESDAY			
THURSDAY			
FRIDAY			
SATURDAY			
SUNDAY			

DATE

DAILY WHY

HEALTH HABITS

☐ Meditation   ☐ 8 Glasses of water

☐ Visualisation   ☐ Stretching

Today, I'm grateful for:

How did I feel in my body today and why?

WORKOUT

....

....

Today's wellness mantra

Breakfast

Snack am

Lunch

Snack pm

Dinner

☐ Meditation ☐ 8 Glasses of water

☐ Visualisation ☐ Stretching

DATE

My intention for today is:

What habits do I most want to improve and why?

Breakfast

Snack am

Lunch

Snack pm

Dinner

WORKOUT

....

....

Today's wellness mantra

DATE

DAILY WHY

HEALTH HABITS

☐ Meditation ☐ 8 Glasses of water

☐ Visualisation ☐ Stretching

What I love about my body is:

In what way did I practice conscious eating today?

WORKOUT

....

....

Today's wellness mantra

Breakfast

Snack am

Lunch

Snack pm

Dinner

HEALTH HABITS

☐ Meditation ☐ 8 Glasses of water

☐ Visualisation ☐ Stretching

DAILY WHY

DATE

Today is my opportunity to:

What did I notice about my mindset today?

Breakfast

Snack am

Lunch

Snack pm

Dinner

WORKOUT

....

....

Today's wellness mantra

☐ Meditation   ☐ 8 Glasses of water

☐ Visualisation   ☐ Stretching

Today is going to be great because:

What was today's lesson?

WORKOUT

....

....

Today's wellness mantra

Breakfast

Snack am

Lunch

Snack pm

Dinner

- [ ] Meditation
- [ ] 8 Glasses of water
- [ ] Visualisation
- [ ] Stretching

DAILY WHY

DATE

Today, I'm excited to create:

How did I show discipline and move closer to my wellness goals today?

Breakfast

Snack am

Lunch

Snack pm

Dinner

WORKOUT

....

....

Today's wellness mantra

WEEKLY CHECK-IN

What goals have I achieved this week?

☐ Review My Wellness
  Goal Planner

☐ Review My Why Statement

☐ Complete My Weekly Planner

What's going well and why is it?

What's most challenging and how can I turn it to my advantage?

How can I drink more water every day?

What do I need to START doing to have better health?

What do I need to STOP doing for better health?

What is one thing I can do this week that will create the biggest results for my health & wellness?

OLD HABIT >	NEW HABIT >	NEW ACTIONS >	NEW AFFIRMATION / MANTRA

WEEKLY PLANNER

Shopping list:

NEW HEALTHY HABIT FOCUS

	BREAKFAST SNACK / WORKOUTS / CLASSES	LUNCH SNACK / WORKOUTS / CLASSES	DINNER SNACK / WORKOUTS / CLASSES
MONDAY			
TUESDAY			
WEDNESDAY			
THURSDAY			
FRIDAY			
SATURDAY			
SUNDAY			

	Meditation		8 Glasses of water
	Visualisation		Stretching

Today, I'm going to focus on being:

What strengths did I use today?

WORKOUT

....

....

Today's wellness mantra

Breakfast

Snack am

Lunch

Snack pm

Dinner

HEALTH HABITS

- [ ] Meditation
- [ ] 8 Glasses of water
- [ ] Visualisation
- [ ] Stretching

DAILY WHY

DATE

Today would be amazing if:

Today, I practised mindfulness when:

Breakfast

Snack am

Lunch

Snack pm

Dinner

WORKOUT

....

....

Today's wellness mantra

DAILY WHY

HEALTH HABITS

☐ Meditation   ☐ 8 Glasses of water

☐ Visualisation   ☐ Stretching

Today, I'm open to the possibility of:

When did I show willpower today?

WORKOUT

....

....

Today's wellness mantra

Breakfast

Snack am

Lunch

Snack pm

Dinner

☐ Meditation   ☐ 8 Glasses of water

☐ Visualisation   ☐ Stretching

DAILY WHY

DATE

Today, I'm going to focus on eating:

What went well today?

Breakfast

Snack am

Lunch

Snack pm

Dinner

WORKOUT

....

....

Today's wellness mantra

DATE

DAILY WHY

HEALTH HABITS

☐ Meditation   ☐ 8 Glasses of water

☐ Visualisation   ☐ Stretching

Today, I'm grateful for:

How did I feel in my body today and why?

WORKOUT

....

....

Today's wellness mantra

Breakfast

Snack am

Lunch

Snack pm

Dinner

HEALTH HABITS

- [ ] Meditation
- [ ] 8 Glasses of water
- [ ] Visualisation
- [ ] Stretching

DAILY WHY

DATE

My intention for today is:

What habits do I most want to improve and why?

Breakfast

Snack am

Lunch

Snack pm

Dinner

WORKOUT

....

....

Today's wellness mantra

WEEKLY CHECK-IN

My week in review

What progress have I made this week?

Where do I see results & why?

What do I need to start or stop?

When do I feel the best in my body and mind?

What does my body need most, right now?

When and how do I sabotage my health and wellness goals?

What is one thing I can do this week that will create the biggest results for my health & wellness?

OLD HABIT >	NEW HABIT >	NEW ACTIONS >	NEW AFFIRMATION / MANTRA

WEEKLY PLANNER

Shopping list:

NEW HEALTHY HABIT FOCUS

	BREAKFAST SNACK / WORKOUTS / CLASSES	LUNCH SNACK / WORKOUTS / CLASSES	DINNER SNACK / WORKOUTS / CLASSES
MONDAY			
TUESDAY			
WEDNESDAY			
THURSDAY			
FRIDAY			
SATURDAY			
SUNDAY			

- [ ] Meditation
- [ ] 8 Glasses of water
- [ ] Visualisation
- [ ] Stretching

What I love about my body is:

In what way did I practice conscious eating today?

WORKOUT

....

....

Today's wellness mantra

Breakfast

Snack am

Lunch

Snack pm

Dinner

HEALTH HABITS

☐ Meditation   ☐ 8 Glasses of water

☐ Visualisation   ☐ Stretching

DAILY WHY

DATE

Today is my opportunity to:

What did I notice about my mindset today?

Breakfast

Snack am

Lunch

Snack pm

Dinner

WORKOUT

....

....

Today's wellness mantra

DATE

HEALTH HABITS

☐ Meditation ☐ 8 Glasses of water

☐ Visualisation ☐ Stretching

Today is going to be great because:

What was today's lesson?

WORKOUT

....

....

Today's wellness mantra

Breakfast

Snack am

Lunch

Snack pm

Dinner

☐ Meditation ☐ 8 Glasses of water

☐ Visualisation ☐ Stretching

DAILY WHY

DATE

Today, I'm excited to create:

How did I show discipline and move closer to my wellness goals today?

Breakfast

Snack am

Lunch

Snack pm

Dinner

WORKOUT

....

....

Today's wellness mantra

☐ Meditation ☐ 8 Glasses of water

☐ Visualisation ☐ Stretching

Today, I'm going to focus on being:

What strengths did I use today?

WORKOUT

....

....

Today's wellness mantra

Breakfast

Snack am

Lunch

Snack pm

Dinner

☐ Meditation ☐ 8 Glasses of water

☐ Visualisation ☐ Stretching

DAILY WHY

DATE

Today would be amazing if:

Today, I practised mindfulness when:

Breakfast

Snack am

Lunch

Snack pm

Dinner

WORKOUT

....

....

Today's wellness mantra

WEEKLY CHECK-IN

My week in review

What major goals have I achieved this month?

Where am I having success and why?

What are the biggest distractions to improving my health and how can I remove them?

What does my body tell me I need to eat more or less of?

Do I eat too much or too little for a strong, healthy body?

What am I enjoying most about my journey to better health?

What is one thing I can do this week that will create the biggest results for my health & wellness?

OLD HABIT >	NEW HABIT >	NEW ACTIONS >	NEW AFFIRMATION / MANTRA

WEEKLY PLANNER

Shopping list:

NEW HEALTHY HABIT FOCUS

	BREAKFAST SNACK / WORKOUTS / CLASSES	LUNCH SNACK / WORKOUTS / CLASSES	DINNER SNACK / WORKOUTS / CLASSES
MONDAY			
TUESDAY			
WEDNESDAY			
THURSDAY			
FRIDAY			
SATURDAY			
SUNDAY			

DATE

HEALTH HABITS

- [ ] Meditation
- [ ] 8 Glasses of water
- [ ] Visualisation
- [ ] Stretching

Today, I'm open to the possibility of:

When did I show willpower today?

WORKOUT

....

....

Today's wellness mantra

Breakfast

Snack am

Lunch

Snack pm

Dinner

- [ ] Meditation
- [ ] 8 Glasses of water
- [ ] Visualisation
- [ ] Stretching

DAILY WHY

DATE

Today, I'm going to focus on eating:

What went well today?

Breakfast

Snack am

Lunch

Snack pm

Dinner

WORKOUT

....

....

Today's wellness mantra

DATE

DAILY WHY

HEALTH HABITS

☐ Meditation ☐ 8 Glasses of water

☐ Visualisation ☐ Stretching

Today, I'm grateful for:

How did I feel in my body today and why?

WORKOUT

....

....

Today's wellness mantra

Breakfast

Snack am

Lunch

Snack pm

Dinner

☐ Meditation   ☐ 8 Glasses of water

☐ Visualisation   ☐ Stretching

DAILY WHY

DATE

My intention for today is:

What habits do I most want to improve and why?

Breakfast

Snack am

Lunch

Snack pm

Dinner

WORKOUT

....

....

Today's wellness mantra

DAILY WHY

HEALTH HABITS

☐ Meditation   ☐ 8 Glasses of water

☐ Visualisation ☐ Stretching

What I love about my body is:

In what way did I practice conscious eating today?

WORKOUT

....

....

Today's wellness mantra

Breakfast

Snack am

Lunch

Snack pm

Dinner

HEALTH HABITS

☐ Meditation ☐ 8 Glasses of water

☐ Visualisation ☐ Stretching

DAILY WHY

DATE

Today is my opportunity to:

What did I notice about my mindset today?

Breakfast

Snack am

Lunch

Snack pm

Dinner

WORKOUT

....

....

Today's wellness mantra

WEEKLY CHECK-IN

What progress have I made this week?

What's working and why is it working?

What's not working and what am I willing to do about it?

What steps can I take to focus my diet on eating more fresh and healthy foods?

What is one thing I can do every day to take care of my body?

What three things do I most enjoy by improving my health?

What is one thing I can do this week that will create the biggest results for my health & wellness?

OLD HABIT >	NEW HABIT >	NEW ACTIONS >	NEW AFFIRMATION / MANTRA

WEEKLY PLANNER

Shopping list:

NEW HEALTHY HABIT FOCUS

	BREAKFAST SNACK / WORKOUTS / CLASSES	LUNCH SNACK / WORKOUTS / CLASSES	DINNER SNACK / WORKOUTS / CLASSES
MONDAY			
TUESDAY			
WEDNESDAY			
THURSDAY			
FRIDAY			
SATURDAY			
SUNDAY			

☐ Meditation   ☐ 8 Glasses of water

☐ Visualisation   ☐ Stretching

Today is going to be great because:

What was today's lesson?

WORKOUT

....

....

Today's wellness mantra

Breakfast

Snack am

Lunch

Snack pm

Dinner

HEALTH HABITS

- [ ] Meditation
- [ ] 8 Glasses of water
- [ ] Visualisation
- [ ] Stretching

DAILY WHY

DATE

Today, I'm excited to create:

How did I show discipline and move closer to my wellness goals today?

Breakfast

Snack am

Lunch

Snack pm

Dinner

WORKOUT

....

....

Today's wellness mantra

Meditation ☐   ☐ 8 Glasses of water

Visualisation ☐   ☐ Stretching

Today, I'm going to focus on being:

What strengths did I use today?

WORKOUT

....

....

Today's wellness mantra

Breakfast

Snack am

Lunch

Snack pm

Dinner

☐ Meditation ☐ 8 Glasses of water

☐ Visualisation ☐ Stretching

DAILY WHY

DATE

Today would be amazing if:

Today, I practised mindfulness when:

Breakfast

Snack am

Lunch

Snack pm

Dinner

WORKOUT

....

....

Today's wellness mantra

☐ Meditation   ☐ 8 Glasses of water

☐ Visualisation   ☐ Stretching

Today, I'm open to the possibility of:

When did I show willpower today?

WORKOUT

....

....

Today's wellness mantra

Breakfast

Snack am

Lunch

Snack pm

Dinner

- [ ] Meditation
- [ ] 8 Glasses of water
- [ ] Visualisation
- [ ] Stretching

Today, I'm going to focus on eating:

What went well today?

Breakfast

Snack am

Lunch

Snack pm

Dinner

WORKOUT

....

....

Today's wellness mantra

WEEKLY CHECK-IN

My week in review

What goals have I achieved this week?

What's going well and why is it?

What's most challenging and how can I turn it to my advantage?

How can I drink more water every day?

What do I need to START doing to have better health?

What do I need to STOP doing for better health?

What is one thing I can do this week that will create the biggest results for my health & wellness?

OLD HABIT >	NEW HABIT >	NEW ACTIONS >	NEW AFFIRMATION / MANTRA

WEEKLY PLANNER

Shopping list:

NEW HEALTHY HABIT FOCUS

	BREAKFAST SNACK / WORKOUTS / CLASSES	LUNCH SNACK / WORKOUTS / CLASSES	DINNER SNACK / WORKOUTS / CLASSES
MONDAY			
TUESDAY			
WEDNESDAY			
THURSDAY			
FRIDAY			
SATURDAY			
SUNDAY			

- [ ] Meditation
- [ ] 8 Glasses of water
- [ ] Visualisation
- [ ] Stretching

Today, I'm grateful for:

How did I feel in my body today and why?

WORKOUT

....

....

Today's wellness mantra

Breakfast

Snack am

Lunch

Snack pm

Dinner

- [ ] Meditation
- [ ] 8 Glasses of water
- [ ] Visualisation
- [ ] Stretching

DAILY WHY

DATE

My intention for today is:

What habits do I most want to improve and why?

Breakfast

Snack am

Lunch

Snack pm

Dinner

WORKOUT

....

....

Today's wellness mantra

DATE

DAILY WHY

HEALTH HABITS

☐ Meditation ☐ 8 Glasses of water

☐ Visualisation ☐ Stretching

What I love about my body is:

In what way did I practice conscious eating today?

WORKOUT

....

....

Today's wellness mantra

Breakfast

Snack am

Lunch

Snack pm

Dinner

- [ ] Meditation
- [ ] 8 Glasses of water
- [ ] Visualisation
- [ ] Stretching

Today is my opportunity to:

What did I notice about my mindset today?

Breakfast

Snack am

Lunch

Snack pm

Dinner

WORKOUT

....

....

Today's wellness mantra

Meditation ☐   8 Glasses of water ☐

Visualisation ☐   Stretching ☐

Today is going to be great because:

What was today's lesson?

WORKOUT

....

....

Today's wellness mantra

Breakfast

Snack am

Lunch

Snack pm

Dinner

- [ ] Meditation
- [ ] 8 Glasses of water
- [ ] Visualisation
- [ ] Stretching

DAILY WHY

DATE

Today, I'm excited to create:

How did I show discipline and move closer to my wellness goals today?

Breakfast

Snack am

Lunch

Snack pm

Dinner

WORKOUT

....

....

Today's wellness mantra

WEEKLY CHECK-IN

My week in review

What progress have I made this week?

☐ Review My Wellness Goal Planner

☐ Review My Why Statement

☐ Complete My Weekly Planner

Where do I see results & why?

What do I need to start or stop?

When do I feel the best in my body and mind?

What does my body need most, right now?

When and how do I sabotage my health and wellness goals?

What is one thing I can do this week that will create the biggest results for my health & wellness?

OLD HABIT >	NEW HABIT >	NEW ACTIONS >	NEW AFFIRMATION / MANTRA

WEEKLY PLANNER

Shopping list:

NEW HEALTHY HABIT FOCUS

	BREAKFAST SNACK / WORKOUTS / CLASSES	LUNCH SNACK / WORKOUTS / CLASSES	DINNER SNACK / WORKOUTS / CLASSES
MONDAY			
TUESDAY			
WEDNESDAY			
THURSDAY			
FRIDAY			
SATURDAY			
SUNDAY			

☐ Meditation   ☐ 8 Glasses of water

☐ Visualisation   ☐ Stretching

Today, I'm going to focus on being: What strengths did I use today?

WORKOUT

....

....

Today's wellness mantra

Breakfast

Snack am

Lunch

Snack pm

Dinner

HEALTH HABITS

☐ Meditation   ☐ 8 Glasses of water

☐ Visualisation   ☐ Stretching

DAILY WHY

DATE

Today would be amazing if:

Today, I practised mindfulness when:

Breakfast

Snack am

Lunch

Snack pm

Dinner

WORKOUT

....

....

Today's wellness mantra

DATE

HEALTH HABITS

☐ Meditation   ☐ 8 Glasses of water

☐ Visualisation   ☐ Stretching

Today, I'm open to the possibility of:

When did I show willpower today?

WORKOUT

....

....

Today's wellness mantra

Breakfast

Snack am

Lunch

Snack pm

Dinner

☐ Meditation   ☐ 8 Glasses of water

☐ Visualisation   ☐ Stretching

DAILY WHY

DATE

Today, I'm going to focus on eating:

What went well today?

Breakfast

Snack am

Lunch

Snack pm

Dinner

WORKOUT

....

....

Today's wellness mantra

DATE

DAILY WHY

HEALTH HABITS

☐ Meditation ☐ 8 Glasses of water

☐ Visualisation ☐ Stretching

Today, I'm grateful for:

How did I feel in my body today and why?

WORKOUT

....

....

Today's wellness mantra

Breakfast

Snack am

Lunch

Snack pm

Dinner

- [ ] Meditation
- [ ] 8 Glasses of water
- [ ] Visualisation
- [ ] Stretching

My intention for today is:

What habits do I most want to improve and why?

Breakfast

Snack am

Lunch

Snack pm

Dinner

WORKOUT

....

....

Today's wellness mantra

WEEKLY CHECK-IN

What major goals have I achieved this month?

☐ Review My Wellness
  Goal Planner

☐ Review My Why Statement

☐ Complete My Weekly Planner

Where am I having success and why?

What are the biggest distractions to improving my health and how can I remove them?

What does my body tell me I need to eat more or less of?

Do I eat too much or too little for a strong, healthy body?

What am I enjoying most about my journey to better health?

What is one thing I can do this week that will create the biggest results for my health & wellness?

OLD HABIT >	NEW HABIT >	NEW ACTIONS >	NEW AFFIRMATION / MANTRA

WEEKLY PLANNER

Shopping list:

NEW HEALTHY HABIT FOCUS

	BREAKFAST SNACK / WORKOUTS / CLASSES	LUNCH SNACK / WORKOUTS / CLASSES	DINNER SNACK / WORKOUTS / CLASSES
MONDAY			
TUESDAY			
WEDNESDAY			
THURSDAY			
FRIDAY			
SATURDAY			
SUNDAY			

DATE	DAILY WHY	HEALTH HABITS

HEALTH HABITS

☐ Meditation ☐ 8 Glasses of water

☐ Visualisation ☐ Stretching

What I love about my body is:

In what way did I practice conscious eating today?

WORKOUT

....

....

Today's wellness mantra

Breakfast

Snack am

Lunch

Snack pm

Dinner

HEALTH HABITS

☐ Meditation   ☐ 8 Glasses of water

☐ Visualisation   ☐ Stretching

DAILY WHY

DATE

Today is my opportunity to:

What did I notice about my mindset today?

Breakfast

Snack am

Lunch

Snack pm

Dinner

WORKOUT

....

....

Today's wellness mantra

DATE

HEALTH HABITS

☐ Meditation ☐ 8 Glasses of water

☐ Visualisation ☐ Stretching

Today is going to be great because:

What was today's lesson?

WORKOUT

....

....

Today's wellness mantra

Breakfast

Snack am

Lunch

Snack pm

Dinner

HEALTH HABITS

☐ Meditation   ☐ 8 Glasses of water

☐ Visualisation   ☐ Stretching

DAILY WHY

DATE

Today, I'm excited to create:

How did I show discipline and move closer to my wellness goals today?

Breakfast

Snack am

Lunch

Snack pm

Dinner

WORKOUT

....

....

Today's wellness mantra

DAILY WHY

HEALTH HABITS

☐ Meditation   ☐ 8 Glasses of water

☐ Visualisation ☐ Stretching

Today, I'm going to focus on being:

What strengths did I use today?

WORKOUT

....

....

Today's wellness mantra

Breakfast

Snack am

Lunch

Snack pm

Dinner

HEALTH HABITS

- [ ] Meditation
- [ ] 8 Glasses of water
- [ ] Visualisation
- [ ] Stretching

DAILY WHY

DATE

Today would be amazing if:

Today, I practised mindfulness when:

Breakfast

Snack am

Lunch

Snack pm

Dinner

WORKOUT

....

....

Today's wellness mantra

WEEKLY CHECK-IN

My week in review

What progress have I made this week?

☐ Review My Wellness Goal Planner

☐ Review My Why Statement

☐ Complete My Weekly Planner

What's working and why is it working?

What's not working and what am I willing to do about it?

What steps can I take to focus my diet on eating more fresh and healthy foods?

What is one thing I can do every day to take care of my body?

What three things do I most enjoy by improving my health?

What is one thing I can do this week that will create the biggest results for my health & wellness?

OLD HABIT >	NEW HABIT >	NEW ACTIONS >	NEW AFFIRMATION / MANTRA

WEEKLY PLANNER

Shopping list:

NEW HEALTHY HABIT FOCUS

	BREAKFAST SNACK / WORKOUTS / CLASSES	LUNCH SNACK / WORKOUTS / CLASSES	DINNER SNACK / WORKOUTS / CLASSES
MONDAY			
TUESDAY			
WEDNESDAY			
THURSDAY			
FRIDAY			
SATURDAY			
SUNDAY			

☐ Meditation   ☐ 8 Glasses of water

☐ Visualisation   ☐ Stretching

Today, I'm open to the possibility of:

When did I show willpower today?

WORKOUT

....

....

Today's wellness mantra

Breakfast

Snack am

Lunch

Snack pm

Dinner

- [ ] Meditation
- [ ] 8 Glasses of water
- [ ] Visualisation
- [ ] Stretching

DAILY WHY

DATE

Today, I'm going to focus on eating:

What went well today?

Breakfast

Snack am

Lunch

Snack pm

Dinner

WORKOUT

....

....

Today's wellness mantra

☐ Meditation   ☐ 8 Glasses of water

☐ Visualisation   ☐ Stretching

Today, I'm grateful for:

How did I feel in my body today and why?

WORKOUT

....

....

Today's wellness mantra

Breakfast

Snack am

Lunch

Snack pm

Dinner

- [ ] Meditation
- [ ] 8 Glasses of water
- [ ] Visualisation
- [ ] Stretching

DAILY WHY

DATE

My intention for today is:

What habits do I most want to improve and why?

Breakfast

Snack am

Lunch

Snack pm

Dinner

WORKOUT

....

....

Today's wellness mantra

DATE

DAILY WHY

HEALTH HABITS

☐ Meditation   ☐ 8 Glasses of water

☐ Visualisation   ☐ Stretching

What I love about my body is:

In what way did I practice conscious eating today?

WORKOUT

....

....

Today's wellness mantra

Breakfast

Snack am

Lunch

Snack pm

Dinner

HEALTH HABITS

- [ ] Meditation
- [ ] 8 Glasses of water
- [ ] Visualisation
- [ ] Stretching

DAILY WHY

Today is my opportunity to:

What did I notice about my mindset today?

Breakfast

Snack am

Lunch

Snack pm

Dinner

WORKOUT

....

....

Today's wellness mantra

WEEKLY CHECK-IN

My week in review

What goals have I achieved this week?

☐ Review My Wellness Goal Planner

☐ Review My Why Statement

☐ Complete My Weekly Planner

What's going well and why is it?

What's most challenging and how can I turn it to my advantage?

How can I drink more water every day?

What do I need to START doing to have better health?

What do I need to STOP doing for better health?

What is one thing I can do this week that will create the biggest results for my health & wellness?

OLD HABIT >	NEW HABIT >	NEW ACTIONS >	NEW AFFIRMATION / MANTRA

WEEKLY PLANNER

Shopping list:

NEW HEALTHY HABIT FOCUS

	BREAKFAST SNACK / WORKOUTS / CLASSES	LUNCH SNACK / WORKOUTS / CLASSES	DINNER SNACK / WORKOUTS / CLASSES
MONDAY			
TUESDAY			
WEDNESDAY			
THURSDAY			
FRIDAY			
SATURDAY			
SUNDAY			

Meditation ☐

8 Glasses of water ☐

Visualisation ☐

Stretching ☐

Today is going to be great because:

What was today's lesson?

WORKOUT

....

....

Today's wellness mantra

Breakfast

Snack am

Lunch

Snack pm

Dinner

- [ ] Meditation
- [ ] 8 Glasses of water
- [ ] Visualisation
- [ ] Stretching

Today, I'm excited to create:

How did I show discipline and move closer to my wellness goals today?

Breakfast

Snack am

Lunch

Snack pm

Dinner

WORKOUT

....

....

Today's wellness mantra

DATE

DAILY WHY

HEALTH HABITS

☐ Meditation   ☐ 8 Glasses of water

☐ Visualisation   ☐ Stretching

Today, I'm going to focus on being:

What strengths did I use today?

WORKOUT

....

....

Today's wellness mantra

Breakfast

Snack am

Lunch

Snack pm

Dinner

☐ Meditation   ☐ 8 Glasses of water

☐ Visualisation   ☐ Stretching

DAILY WHY

DATE

Today would be amazing if:

Today, I practised mindfulness when:

Breakfast

Snack am

Lunch

Snack pm

Dinner

WORKOUT

....

....

Today's wellness mantra

DATE

HEALTH HABITS

☐ Meditation   ☐ 8 Glasses of water

☐ Visualisation   ☐ Stretching

Today, I'm open to the possibility of:

When did I show willpower today?

WORKOUT

....

....

Today's wellness mantra

Breakfast

Snack am

Lunch

Snack pm

Dinner

DAILY WHY

DATE

- [ ] Meditation
- [ ] 8 Glasses of water
- [ ] Visualisation
- [ ] Stretching

Today, I'm going to focus on eating:

What went well today?

Breakfast

Snack am

Lunch

Snack pm

Dinner

WORKOUT

....

....

Today's wellness mantra

WEEKLY CHECK-IN

My week in review

What progress have I made this week?

☐ Review My Wellness Goal Planner

☐ Review My Why Statement

☐ Complete My Weekly Planner

Where do I see results & why?

What do I need to start or stop?

When do I feel the best in my body and mind?

What does my body need most, right now?

When and how do I sabotage my health and wellness goals?

What is one thing I can do this week that will create the biggest results for my health & wellness?

OLD HABIT >	NEW HABIT >	NEW ACTIONS >	NEW AFFIRMATION / MANTRA

WEEKLY PLANNER

Shopping list:

NEW HEALTHY HABIT FOCUS

	BREAKFAST SNACK / WORKOUTS / CLASSES	LUNCH SNACK / WORKOUTS / CLASSES	DINNER SNACK / WORKOUTS / CLASSES
MONDAY			
TUESDAY			
WEDNESDAY			
THURSDAY			
FRIDAY			
SATURDAY			
SUNDAY			

DAILY WHY

HEALTH HABITS

☐ Meditation ☐ 8 Glasses of water

☐ Visualisation ☐ Stretching

Today, I'm grateful for:

How did I feel in my body today and why?

WORKOUT

....

....

Today's wellness mantra

Breakfast

Snack am

Lunch

Snack pm

Dinner

HEALTH HABITS

☐ Meditation   ☐ 8 Glasses of water

☐ Visualisation   ☐ Stretching

DAILY WHY

DATE

My intention for today is:

What habits do I most want to improve and why?

Breakfast

Snack am

Lunch

Snack pm

Dinner

WORKOUT

....

....

Today's wellness mantra

DATE

DAILY WHY

HEALTH HABITS

☐ Meditation   ☐ 8 Glasses of water

☐ Visualisation   ☐ Stretching

What I love about my body is:

In what way did I practice conscious eating today?

WORKOUT

....

....

Today's wellness mantra

Breakfast

Snack am

Lunch

Snack pm

Dinner

☐ Meditation ☐ 8 Glasses of water

☐ Visualisation ☐ Stretching

DAILY WHY

DATE

Today is my opportunity to:

What did I notice about my mindset today?

Breakfast

Snack am

Lunch

Snack pm

Dinner

WORKOUT

....

....

Today's wellness mantra

Meditation ☐   8 Glasses of water ☐

Visualisation ☐   Stretching ☐

Today is going to be great because:

What was today's lesson?

WORKOUT

....

....

Today's wellness mantra

Breakfast

Snack am

Lunch

Snack pm

Dinner

HEALTH HABITS

- [ ] Meditation
- [ ] Visualisation
- [ ] 8 Glasses of water
- [ ] Stretching

DAILY WHY

DATE

Today, I'm excited to create:

How did I show discipline and move closer to my wellness goals today?

Breakfast

Snack am

Lunch

Snack pm

Dinner

WORKOUT

....

....

Today's wellness mantra

WEEKLY CHECK-IN

My week in review

What major goals have I achieved this month?

Where am I having success and why?

What are the biggest distractions to improving my health and how can I remove them?

What does my body tell me I need to eat more or less of?

Do I eat too much or too little for a strong, healthy body?

What am I enjoying most about my journey to better health?

What is one thing I can do this week that will create the biggest results for my health & wellness?

OLD HABIT >	NEW HABIT >	NEW ACTIONS >	NEW AFFIRMATION / MANTRA

WEEKLY PLANNER

Shopping list:

	BREAKFAST SNACK / WORKOUTS / CLASSES	LUNCH SNACK / WORKOUTS / CLASSES	DINNER SNACK / WORKOUTS / CLASSES
MONDAY			
TUESDAY			
WEDNESDAY			
THURSDAY			
FRIDAY			
SATURDAY			
SUNDAY			

DATE

DAILY WHY

HEALTH HABITS

☐ Meditation ☐ 8 Glasses of water

☐ Visualisation ☐ Stretching

Today, I'm going to focus on being:

What strengths did I use today?

WORKOUT

....

....

Today's wellness mantra

Breakfast

Snack am

Lunch

Snack pm

Dinner

☐ Meditation ☐ 8 Glasses of water

☐ Visualisation ☐ Stretching

DAILY WHY

DATE

Today would be amazing if:

Today, I practised mindfulness when:

Breakfast

Snack am

Lunch

Snack pm

Dinner

WORKOUT

....

....

Today's wellness mantra

☐ Meditation   ☐ 8 Glasses of water

☐ Visualisation   ☐ Stretching

Today, I'm open to the possibility of:

When did I show willpower today?

WORKOUT

....

....

Today's wellness mantra

Breakfast

Snack am

Lunch

Snack pm

Dinner

HEALTH HABITS

- ☐ Meditation
- ☐ 8 Glasses of water
- ☐ Visualisation
- ☐ Stretching

DAILY WHY

DATE

Today, I'm going to focus on eating:

What went well today?

Breakfast

Snack am

Lunch

Snack pm

Dinner

WORKOUT

....

....

Today's wellness mantra

DATE

HEALTH HABITS

☐ Meditation ☐ 8 Glasses of water

☐ Visualisation ☐ Stretching

Today, I'm grateful for:

How did I feel in my body today and why?

WORKOUT

....

....

Today's wellness mantra

Breakfast

Snack am

Lunch

Snack pm

Dinner

HEALTH HABITS

☐ Meditation   ☐ 8 Glasses of water

☐ Visualisation   ☐ Stretching

DAILY WHY

DATE

My intention for today is:

What habits do I most want to improve and why?

Breakfast

Snack am

Lunch

Snack pm

Dinner

WORKOUT

....

....

Today's wellness mantra

WEEKLY CHECK-IN

What progress have I made this week?

☐ Review My Wellness Goal Planner

☐ Review My Why Statement

☐ Complete My Weekly Planner

What's working and why is it working?

What's not working and what am I willing to do about it?

What steps can I take to focus my diet on eating more fresh and healthy foods?

What is one thing I can do every day to take care of my body?

What three things do I most enjoy by improving my health?

What is one thing I can do this week that will create the biggest results for my health & wellness?

OLD HABIT >	NEW HABIT >	NEW ACTIONS >	NEW AFFIRMATION / MANTRA

WEEKLY PLANNER

Shopping list:

NEW HEALTHY HABIT FOCUS

	BREAKFAST SNACK / WORKOUTS / CLASSES	LUNCH SNACK / WORKOUTS / CLASSES	DINNER SNACK / WORKOUTS / CLASSES
MONDAY			
TUESDAY			
WEDNESDAY			
THURSDAY			
FRIDAY			
SATURDAY			
SUNDAY			

DATE

DAILY WHY

HEALTH HABITS

☐ Meditation ☐ 8 Glasses of water

☐ Visualisation ☐ Stretching

What I love about my body is:

In what way did I practice conscious eating today?

WORKOUT

....

....

Today's wellness mantra

Breakfast

Snack am

Lunch

Snack pm

Dinner

☐ Meditation   ☐ 8 Glasses of water

☐ Visualisation   ☐ Stretching

DAILY WHY

DATE

Today is my opportunity to:

What did I notice about my mindset today?

Breakfast

Snack am

Lunch

Snack pm

Dinner

WORKOUT

....

....

Today's wellness mantra

DATE

HEALTH HABITS

☐ Meditation   ☐ 8 Glasses of water

☐ Visualisation   ☐ Stretching

Today is going to be great because:

What was today's lesson?

WORKOUT

....

....

Today's wellness mantra

Breakfast

Snack am

Lunch

Snack pm

Dinner

- [ ] Meditation
- [ ] 8 Glasses of water
- [ ] Visualisation
- [ ] Stretching

DAILY WHY

DATE

Today, I'm excited to create:

How did I show discipline and move closer to my wellness goals today?

Breakfast

Snack am

Lunch

Snack pm

Dinner

WORKOUT

....

....

Today's wellness mantra

DATE	DAILY WHY	HEALTH HABITS

HEALTH HABITS

☐ Meditation   ☐ 8 Glasses of water

☐ Visualisation   ☐ Stretching

Today, I'm going to focus on being:

What strengths did I use today?

WORKOUT

....

....

Today's wellness mantra

Breakfast

Snack am

Lunch

Snack pm

Dinner

HEALTH HABITS

- [ ] Meditation
- [ ] Visualisation
- [ ] 8 Glasses of water
- [ ] Stretching

DAILY WHY

DATE

Today would be amazing if:

Today, I practised mindfulness when:

Breakfast

Snack am

Lunch

Snack pm

Dinner

WORKOUT

....

....

Today's wellness mantra

90 DAY REVIEW

What goals have I completed this past 90 days that have improved my health and wellness? How do I feel?

....

....

What's going well and why?
What mindset changes do I wish to make around my health and wellness?
What is no longer acceptable to me?

....

....

What do I need to STOP doing?

....

....

What do I need to START doing?

....

....

What limiting beliefs are holding me back from personal growth and better wellbeing?

....

....

What decisions do I need to make that I have been putting off around my health?

....

....

What activities do I spend my time on and how do they contribute to my health and wellness?

....

....

What new health goal am I focusing on for the next 90 days?
What would I love to achieve?

....

....

....

....

☐ Review My Wellness Goal Planner   ☐ Check My Healthy Habits   ☐ Plan My Week

☐ Review My Why Statement   ☐ Complete My 90 Day Planner   ☐ Celebrate My Progress

90 DAY PLANNER

My goals for the next 90 days

Goal:

Target date:

Actions to complete this goal:

WHY I'D LOVE TO ACHIEVE THIS GOAL:

HOW WILL I FEEL WHEN I'VE REACHED THIS GOAL?

Goal:

Target date:

Actions to complete this goal:

WHY I'D LOVE TO ACHIEVE THIS GOAL:

HOW WILL I FEEL WHEN I'VE REACHED THIS GOAL?

Goal:

Target date:

Actions to complete this goal:

WHY I'D LOVE TO ACHIEVE THIS GOAL:

HOW WILL I FEEL WHEN I'VE REACHED THIS GOAL?

Goal:

Target date:

Actions to complete this goal:

WHY I'D LOVE TO ACHIEVE THIS GOAL:

HOW WILL I FEEL WHEN I'VE REACHED THIS GOAL?

EATING WELL IS A FORM OF SELF-RESPECT.

WEEKLY PLANNER

Shopping list:

	BREAKFAST SNACK / WORKOUTS / CLASSES	LUNCH SNACK / WORKOUTS / CLASSES	DINNER SNACK / WORKOUTS / CLASSES
MONDAY			
TUESDAY			
WEDNESDAY			
THURSDAY			
FRIDAY			
SATURDAY			
SUNDAY			

DATE

DAILY WHY

HEALTH HABITS

☐ Meditation   ☐ 8 Glasses of water

☐ Visualisation   ☐ Stretching

Today, I'm grateful for:

How did I feel in my body today and why?

WORKOUT

....

....

Today's wellness mantra

Breakfast

Snack am

Lunch

Snack pm

Dinner

HEALTH HABITS

- [ ] Meditation
- [ ] 8 Glasses of water
- [ ] Visualisation
- [ ] Stretching

DAILY WHY

DATE

My intention for today is:

What habits do I most want to improve and why?

Breakfast

Snack am

Lunch

Snack pm

Dinner

WORKOUT

....

....

Today's wellness mantra

☐ Meditation   ☐ 8 Glasses of water

☐ Visualisation   ☐ Stretching

What I love about my body is:

In what way did I practice conscious eating today?

WORKOUT

....

....

Today's wellness mantra

Breakfast

Snack am

Lunch

Snack pm

Dinner

HEALTH HABITS

- [ ] Meditation
- [ ] 8 Glasses of water
- [ ] Visualisation
- [ ] Stretching

DAILY WHY

DATE

Today is my opportunity to:

What did I notice about my mindset today?

Breakfast

Snack am

Lunch

Snack pm

Dinner

WORKOUT

....

....

Today's wellness mantra

DAILY WHY

HEALTH HABITS

☐ Meditation ☐ 8 Glasses of water

☐ Visualisation ☐ Stretching

Today is going to be great because:

What was today's lesson?

WORKOUT

....

....

Today's wellness mantra

Breakfast

Snack am

Lunch

Snack pm

Dinner

HEALTH HABITS

☐ Meditation ☐ 8 Glasses of water

☐ Visualisation ☐ Stretching

DAILY WHY

DATE

Today, I'm excited to create:

How did I show discipline and move closer to my wellness goals today?

Breakfast

Snack am

Lunch

Snack pm

Dinner

WORKOUT

Today's wellness mantra

WEEKLY CHECK-IN

My week in review

What goals have I achieved this week?

☐ **Review My Wellness Goal Planner**

☐ **Review My Why Statement**

☐ **Complete My Weekly Planner**

What's going well and why is it?

What's most challenging and how can I turn it to my advantage?

How can I drink more water every day?

What do I need to START doing to have better health?

What do I need to STOP doing for better health?

What is one thing I can do this week that will create the biggest results for my health & wellness?

OLD HABIT >	NEW HABIT >	NEW ACTIONS >	NEW AFFIRMATION / MANTRA

WEEKLY PLANNER

Shopping list:

NEW HEALTHY HABIT FOCUS

	BREAKFAST SNACK / WORKOUTS / CLASSES	LUNCH SNACK / WORKOUTS / CLASSES	DINNER SNACK / WORKOUTS / CLASSES
MONDAY			
TUESDAY			
WEDNESDAY			
THURSDAY			
FRIDAY			
SATURDAY			
SUNDAY			

HEALTH HABITS

☐ Meditation ☐ 8 Glasses of water

☐ Visualisation ☐ Stretching

Today, I'm going to focus on being:

What strengths did I use today?

WORKOUT
....
....

Today's wellness mantra

Breakfast

Snack am

Lunch

Snack pm

Dinner

☐ Meditation   ☐ 8 Glasses of water

☐ Visualisation   ☐ Stretching

DAILY WHY

DATE

Today would be amazing if:

Today, I practised mindfulness when:

Breakfast

Snack am

Lunch

Snack pm

Dinner

WORKOUT

....

....

Today's wellness mantra

DATE

DAILY WHY

HEALTH HABITS

☐ Meditation   ☐ 8 Glasses of water

☐ Visualisation   ☐ Stretching

Today, I'm open to the possibility of:

When did I show willpower today?

WORKOUT

....

....

Today's wellness mantra

Breakfast

Snack am

Lunch

Snack pm

Dinner

HEALTH HABITS

☐ Meditation ☐ 8 Glasses of water

☐ Visualisation ☐ Stretching

DAILY WHY

DATE

Today, I'm going to focus on eating:

What went well today?

Breakfast

Snack am

Lunch

Snack pm

Dinner

WORKOUT

....

....

Today's wellness mantra

DATE

DAILY WHY

HEALTH HABITS

☐ Meditation   ☐ 8 Glasses of water

☐ Visualisation   ☐ Stretching

Today, I'm grateful for:

How did I feel in my body today and why?

WORKOUT

....

....

Today's wellness mantra

Breakfast

Snack am

Lunch

Snack pm

Dinner

- [ ] Meditation
- [ ] 8 Glasses of water
- [ ] Visualisation
- [ ] Stretching

DAILY WHY

DATE

My intention for today is:

What habits do I most want to improve and why?

Breakfast

Snack am

Lunch

Snack pm

Dinner

WORKOUT

....

....

Today's wellness mantra

WEEKLY CHECK-IN

What progress have I made this week?

☐ Review My Wellness Goal Planner

☐ Review My Why Statement

☐ Complete My Weekly Planner

Where do I see results & why?

What do I need to start or stop?

When do I feel the best in my body and mind?

What does my body need most, right now?

When and how do I sabotage my health and wellness goals?

What is one thing I can do this week that will create the biggest results for my health & wellness?

OLD HABIT >	NEW HABIT >	NEW ACTIONS >	NEW AFFIRMATION / MANTRA

WEEKLY PLANNER

Shopping list:

NEW HEALTHY HABIT FOCUS

	BREAKFAST SNACK / WORKOUTS / CLASSES	LUNCH SNACK / WORKOUTS / CLASSES	DINNER SNACK / WORKOUTS / CLASSES
MONDAY			
TUESDAY			
WEDNESDAY			
THURSDAY			
FRIDAY			
SATURDAY			
SUNDAY			

DATE

DAILY WHY

HEALTH HABITS

☐ Meditation   ☐ 8 Glasses of water

☐ Visualisation   ☐ Stretching

What I love about my body is:

In what way did I practice conscious eating today?

WORKOUT

....

....

Today's wellness mantra

Breakfast

Snack am

Lunch

Snack pm

Dinner

Meditation ☐   8 Glasses of water ☐

Visualisation ☐   Stretching ☐

DAILY WHY

DATE

Today is my opportunity to:

What did I notice about my mindset today?

Breakfast

Snack am

Lunch

Snack pm

Dinner

WORKOUT

....

....

Today's wellness mantra

DAILY WHY

HEALTH HABITS

☐ Meditation ☐ 8 Glasses of water

☐ Visualisation ☐ Stretching

Today is going to be great because:

What was today's lesson?

WORKOUT

....

....

Today's wellness mantra

Breakfast

Snack am

Lunch

Snack pm

Dinner

- [ ] Meditation
- [ ] 8 Glasses of water
- [ ] Visualisation
- [ ] Stretching

DAILY WHY

DATE

Today, I'm excited to create:

How did I show discipline and move closer to my wellness goals today?

Breakfast

Snack am

Lunch

Snack pm

Dinner

WORKOUT

Today's wellness mantra

DATE

DAILY WHY

HEALTH HABITS

☐ Meditation   ☐ 8 Glasses of water

☐ Visualisation   ☐ Stretching

Today, I'm going to focus on being:

What strengths did I use today?

WORKOUT

....

....

Today's wellness mantra

Breakfast

Snack am

Lunch

Snack pm

Dinner

☐ Meditation ☐ 8 Glasses of water

☐ Visualisation ☐ Stretching

Today would be amazing if:

Today, I practised mindfulness when:

Breakfast

Snack am

Lunch

Snack pm

Dinner

WORKOUT

Today's wellness mantra

WEEKLY CHECK-IN

My week in review

What major goals have I achieved this month?

☐ **Review My Wellness Goal Planner**

☐ **Review My Why Statement**

☐ **Complete My Weekly Planner**

Where am I having success and why?

What are the biggest distractions to improving my health and how can I remove them?

What does my body tell me I need to eat more or less of?

Do I eat too much or too little for a strong, healthy body?

What am I enjoying most about my journey to better health?

What is one thing I can do this week that will create the biggest results for my health & wellness?

OLD HABIT >	NEW HABIT >	NEW ACTIONS >	NEW AFFIRMATION / MANTRA

WEEKLY PLANNER

Shopping List:

NEW HEALTHY HABIT FOCUS

	BREAKFAST SNACK / WORKOUTS / CLASSES	LUNCH SNACK / WORKOUTS / CLASSES	DINNER SNACK / WORKOUTS / CLASSES
MONDAY			
TUESDAY			
WEDNESDAY			
THURSDAY			
FRIDAY			
SATURDAY			
SUNDAY			

Meditation   8 Glasses of water

Visualisation   Stretching

Today, I'm open to the possibility of:

When did I show willpower today?

WORKOUT

....

....

Today's wellness mantra

Breakfast

Snack am

Lunch

Snack pm

Dinner

☐ Meditation ☐ 8 Glasses of water

☐ Visualisation ☐ Stretching

DAILY WHY

DATE

Today, I'm going to focus on eating:

What went well today?

Breakfast

Snack am

Lunch

Snack pm

Dinner

WORKOUT

....

....

Today's wellness mantra

DATE

HEALTH HABITS

☐ Meditation   ☐ 8 Glasses of water

☐ Visualisation   ☐ Stretching

Today, I'm grateful for:

How did I feel in my body today and why?

WORKOUT

....

....

Today's wellness mantra

Breakfast

Snack am

Lunch

Snack pm

Dinner

HEALTH HABITS

☐ Meditation   ☐ 8 Glasses of water

☐ Visualisation   ☐ Stretching

DAILY WHY

DATE

My intention for today is:

What habits do I most want to improve and why?

Breakfast

Snack am

Lunch

Snack pm

Dinner

WORKOUT

Today's wellness mantra

- [ ] Meditation
- [ ] 8 Glasses of water
- [ ] Visualisation
- [ ] Stretching

What I love about my body is:

In what way did I practice conscious eating today?

WORKOUT

Breakfast

Snack am

Lunch

Today's wellness mantra

Snack pm

Dinner

☐ Meditation   ☐ 8 Glasses of water

☐ Visualisation   ☐ Stretching

DAILY WHY

DATE

Today is my opportunity to:

What did I notice about my mindset today?

Breakfast

Snack am

Lunch

Snack pm

Dinner

WORKOUT

....

....

Today's wellness mantra

WEEKLY CHECK-IN

My week in review

What progress have I made this week?

- [ ] Review My Wellness Goal Planner
- [ ] Review My Why Statement
- [ ] Complete My Weekly Planner

What's working and why is it working?

What's not working and what am I willing to do about it?

What steps can I take to focus my diet on eating more fresh and healthy foods?

What is one thing I can do every day to take care of my body?

What three things do I most enjoy by improving my health?

What is one thing I can do this week that will create the biggest results for my health & wellness?

OLD HABIT >	NEW HABIT >	NEW ACTIONS >	NEW AFFIRMATION / MANTRA

WEEKLY PLANNER

Shopping list:

	BREAKFAST SNACK / WORKOUTS / CLASSES	LUNCH SNACK / WORKOUTS / CLASSES	DINNER SNACK / WORKOUTS / CLASSES
MONDAY			
TUESDAY			
WEDNESDAY			
THURSDAY			
FRIDAY			
SATURDAY			
SUNDAY			

- [ ] Meditation
- [ ] 8 Glasses of water
- [ ] Visualisation
- [ ] Stretching

Today is going to be great because:

What was today's lesson?

WORKOUT

....

....

Today's wellness mantra

Breakfast

Snack am

Lunch

Snack pm

Dinner

HEALTH HABITS

☐ Meditation ☐ 8 Glasses of water

☐ Visualisation ☐ Stretching

DAILY WHY

DATE

Today, I'm excited to create:

How did I show discipline and move closer to my wellness goals today?

Breakfast

Snack am

Lunch

Snack pm

Dinner

WORKOUT

....

....

Today's wellness mantra

DATE

DAILY WHY

HEALTH HABITS

- [ ] Meditation
- [ ] 8 Glasses of water
- [ ] Visualisation
- [ ] Stretching

Today, I'm going to focus on being:

What strengths did I use today?

WORKOUT

....

....

Today's wellness mantra

Breakfast

Snack am

Lunch

Snack pm

Dinner

HEALTH HABITS

☐ Meditation   ☐ 8 Glasses of water

☐ Visualisation   ☐ Stretching

DAILY WHY

DATE

Today would be amazing if:

Today, I practised mindfulness when:

Breakfast

Snack am

Lunch

Snack pm

Dinner

WORKOUT

....

....

Today's wellness mantra

DATE

DAILY WHY

HEALTH HABITS

☐ Meditation   ☐ 8 Glasses of water

☐ Visualisation ☐ Stretching

Today, I'm open to the possibility of:

When did I show willpower today?

WORKOUT

....

....

Today's wellness mantra

Breakfast

Snack am

Lunch

Snack pm

Dinner

☐ Meditation   ☐ 8 Glasses of water

☐ Visualisation   ☐ Stretching

DAILY WHY

DATE

Today, I'm going to focus on eating:

What went well today?

Breakfast

Snack am

Lunch

Snack pm

Dinner

WORKOUT

Today's wellness mantra

WEEKLY CHECK-IN

My week in review

What goals have I achieved this week?

☐ Review My Wellness Goal Planner

☐ Review My Why Statement

☐ Complete My Weekly Planner

What's going well and why is it?

What's most challenging and how can I turn it to my advantage?

How can I drink more water every day?

What do I need to START doing to have better health?

What do I need to STOP doing for better health?

What is one thing I can do this week that will create the biggest results for my health & wellness?

OLD HABIT >	NEW HABIT >	NEW ACTIONS >	NEW AFFIRMATION / MANTRA

WEEKLY PLANNER

Shopping list:

NEW HEALTHY HABIT FOCUS

	BREAKFAST SNACK / WORKOUTS / CLASSES	LUNCH SNACK / WORKOUTS / CLASSES	DINNER SNACK / WORKOUTS / CLASSES
MONDAY			
TUESDAY			
WEDNESDAY			
THURSDAY			
FRIDAY			
SATURDAY			
SUNDAY			

DATE

DAILY WHY

HEALTH HABITS

☐ Meditation   ☐ 8 Glasses of water

☐ Visualisation   ☐ Stretching

Today, I'm grateful for:

How did I feel in my body today and why?

WORKOUT

....

....

Today's wellness mantra

Breakfast

Snack am

Lunch

Snack pm

Dinner

HEALTH HABITS

- [ ] Meditation
- [ ] 8 Glasses of water
- [ ] Visualisation
- [ ] Stretching

DAILY WHY

My intention for today is:

What habits do I most want to improve and why?

Breakfast

Snack am

Lunch

Snack pm

Dinner

WORKOUT

Today's wellness mantra

DATE

DAILY WHY

HEALTH HABITS

☐ Meditation   ☐ 8 Glasses of water

☐ Visualisation   ☐ Stretching

What I love about my body is:

In what way did I practice conscious eating today?

WORKOUT

....

....

Today's wellness mantra

Breakfast

Snack am

Lunch

Snack pm

Dinner

HEALTH HABITS

☐ Meditation   ☐ 8 Glasses of water

☐ Visualisation ☐ Stretching

DAILY WHY

DATE

Today is my opportunity to:

What did I notice about my mindset today?

Breakfast

Snack am

Lunch

Snack pm

Dinner

WORKOUT

....

....

Today's wellness mantra

DATE

DAILY WHY

HEALTH HABITS

☐ Meditation ☐ 8 Glasses of water

☐ Visualisation ☐ Stretching

Today is going to be great because:

What was today's lesson?

WORKOUT

Breakfast

Snack am

Lunch

Today's wellness mantra

Snack pm

Dinner

HEALTH HABITS

- [ ] Meditation
- [ ] 8 Glasses of water
- [ ] Visualisation
- [ ] Stretching

DAILY WHY

DATE

Today, I'm excited to create:

How did I show discipline and move closer to my wellness goals today?

Breakfast

Snack am

Lunch

Snack pm

Dinner

WORKOUT

Today's wellness mantra

WEEKLY CHECK-IN

My week in review

What progress have I made this week?

☐ Review My Wellness Goal Planner

☐ Review My Why Statement

☐ Complete My Weekly Planner

Where do I see results & why?

What do I need to start or stop?

When do I feel the best in my body and mind?

What does my body need most, right now?

When and how do I sabotage my health and wellness goals?

What is one thing I can do this week that will create the biggest results for my health & wellness?

OLD HABIT >	NEW HABIT >	NEW ACTIONS >	NEW AFFIRMATION / MANTRA

WEEKLY PLANNER

Shopping list:

NEW HEALTHY HABIT FOCUS

	BREAKFAST SNACK / WORKOUTS / CLASSES	LUNCH SNACK / WORKOUTS / CLASSES	DINNER SNACK / WORKOUTS / CLASSES
MONDAY			
TUESDAY			
WEDNESDAY			
THURSDAY			
FRIDAY			
SATURDAY			
SUNDAY			

- [ ] Meditation
- [ ] 8 Glasses of water
- [ ] Visualisation
- [ ] Stretching

Today, I'm going to focus on being:

What strengths did I use today?

WORKOUT

....

....

Today's wellness mantra

Breakfast

Snack am

Lunch

Snack pm

Dinner

HEALTH HABITS

☐ Meditation   ☐ 8 Glasses of water

☐ Visualisation   ☐ Stretching

DAILY WHY

DATE

Today would be amazing if:

Today, I practised mindfulness when:

Breakfast

Snack am

Lunch

Snack pm

Dinner

WORKOUT

Today's wellness mantra

DATE

DAILY WHY

HEALTH HABITS

- [ ] Meditation
- [ ] 8 Glasses of water
- [ ] Visualisation
- [ ] Stretching

Today, I'm open to the possibility of:

When did I show willpower today?

WORKOUT

....

....

Today's wellness mantra

Breakfast

Snack am

Lunch

Snack pm

Dinner

HEALTH HABITS

- [ ] Meditation
- [ ] Visualisation
- [ ] 8 Glasses of water
- [ ] Stretching

DAILY WHY

DATE

Today, I'm going to focus on eating:

What went well today?

Breakfast

Snack am

Lunch

Snack pm

Dinner

WORKOUT

....

....

Today's wellness mantra

DATE

DAILY WHY

HEALTH HABITS

☐ Meditation ☐ 8 Glasses of water

☐ Visualisation ☐ Stretching

Today, I'm grateful for:

How did I feel in my body today and why?

WORKOUT

....

....

Today's wellness mantra

Breakfast

Snack am

Lunch

Snack pm

Dinner

HEALTH HABITS

☐ Meditation ☐ 8 Glasses of water

☐ Visualisation ☐ Stretching

DAILY WHY

DATE

My intention for today is:

What habits do I most want to improve and why?

Breakfast

Snack am

Lunch

Snack pm

Dinner

WORKOUT

....

....

Today's wellness mantra

WEEKLY CHECK-IN

My week in review

What major goals have I achieved this month?

☐ Review My Wellness Goal Planner

☐ Review My Why Statement

☐ Complete My Weekly Planner

Where am I having success and why?

What are the biggest distractions to improving my health and how can I remove them?

What does my body tell me I need to eat more or less of?

Do I eat too much or too little for a strong, healthy body?

What am I enjoying most about my journey to better health?

What is one thing I can do this week that will create the biggest results for my health & wellness?

OLD HABIT >	NEW HABIT >	NEW ACTIONS >	NEW AFFIRMATION / MANTRA

WEEKLY PLANNER

Shopping list:

NEW HEALTHY HABIT FOCUS

	BREAKFAST SNACK / WORKOUTS / CLASSES	LUNCH SNACK / WORKOUTS / CLASSES	DINNER SNACK / WORKOUTS / CLASSES
MONDAY			
TUESDAY			
WEDNESDAY			
THURSDAY			
FRIDAY			
SATURDAY			
SUNDAY			

☐ Meditation   ☐ 8 Glasses of water

☐ Visualisation   ☐ Stretching

What I love about my body is:

In what way did I practice conscious eating today?

WORKOUT

....

....

Today's wellness mantra

Breakfast

Snack am

Lunch

Snack pm

Dinner

☐ Meditation   ☐ 8 Glasses of water

☐ Visualisation   ☐ Stretching

DAILY WHY

DATE

Today is my opportunity to:

What did I notice about my mindset today?

Breakfast

Snack am

Lunch

Snack pm

Dinner

WORKOUT

Today's wellness mantra

DATE

DAILY WHY

HEALTH HABITS

☐ Meditation ☐ 8 Glasses of water

☐ Visualisation ☐ Stretching

Today is going to be great because:

What was today's lesson?

WORKOUT

....

....

Today's wellness mantra

Breakfast

Snack am

Lunch

Snack pm

Dinner

HEALTH HABITS

☐ Meditation   ☐ 8 Glasses of water

☐ Visualisation   ☐ Stretching

DAILY WHY

DATE

Today, I'm excited to create:

How did I show discipline and move closer to my wellness goals today?

Breakfast

Snack am

Lunch

Snack pm

Dinner

WORKOUT

....

....

Today's wellness mantra

DAILY WHY

HEALTH HABITS

☐ Meditation   ☐ 8 Glasses of water

☐ Visualisation   ☐ Stretching

Today, I'm going to focus on being:

What strengths did I use today?

WORKOUT

....

....

Today's wellness mantra

Breakfast

Snack am

Lunch

Snack pm

Dinner

HEALTH HABITS

☐ Meditation   ☐ 8 Glasses of water

☐ Visualisation   ☐ Stretching

DAILY WHY

DATE

Today would be amazing if:

Today, I practised mindfulness when:

Breakfast

Snack am

Lunch

Snack pm

Dinner

WORKOUT

....

....

Today's wellness mantra

WEEKLY CHECK-IN

My week in review

What progress have I made this week?

☐ Review My Wellness Goal Planner

☐ Review My Why Statement

☐ Complete My Weekly Planner

What's working and why is it working?

What's not working and what am I willing to do about it?

What steps can I take to focus my diet on eating more fresh and healthy foods?

What is one thing I can do every day to take care of my body?

What three things do I most enjoy by improving my health?

What is one thing I can do this week that will create the biggest results for my health & wellness?

OLD HABIT >	NEW HABIT >	NEW ACTIONS >	NEW AFFIRMATION / MANTRA

WEEKLY PLANNER

Shopping list:

NEW HEALTHY HABIT FOCUS

	BREAKFAST SNACK / WORKOUTS / CLASSES	LUNCH SNACK / WORKOUTS / CLASSES	DINNER SNACK / WORKOUTS / CLASSES
MONDAY			
TUESDAY			
WEDNESDAY			
THURSDAY			
FRIDAY			
SATURDAY			
SUNDAY			

DATE

DAILY WHY

HEALTH HABITS

☐ Meditation ☐ 8 Glasses of water

☐ Visualisation ☐ Stretching

Today, I'm open to the possibility of:

When did I show willpower today?

WORKOUT

....

....

Today's wellness mantra

Breakfast

Snack am

Lunch

Snack pm

Dinner

- [ ] Meditation
- [ ] 8 Glasses of water
- [ ] Visualisation
- [ ] Stretching

DAILY WHY

DATE

Today, I'm going to focus on eating:

What went well today?

Breakfast

Snack am

Lunch

Snack pm

Dinner

WORKOUT

....

....

Today's wellness mantra

DATE

DAILY WHY

HEALTH HABITS

☐ Meditation   ☐ 8 Glasses of water

☐ Visualisation   ☐ Stretching

Today, I'm grateful for:

How did I feel in my body today and why?

WORKOUT

....

....

Today's wellness mantra

Breakfast

Snack am

Lunch

Snack pm

Dinner

☐ Meditation ☐ 8 Glasses of water

☐ Visualisation ☐ Stretching

My intention for today is:

What habits do I most want to improve and why?

Breakfast

Snack am

Lunch

Snack pm

Dinner

WORKOUT

Today's wellness mantra

DAILY WHY

HEALTH HABITS

☐ Meditation   ☐ 8 Glasses of water

☐ Visualisation ☐ Stretching

What I love about my body is:

In what way did I practice conscious eating today?

WORKOUT

....

....

Today's wellness mantra

Breakfast

Snack am

Lunch

Snack pm

Dinner

HEALTH HABITS

- [ ] Meditation
- [ ] 8 Glasses of water
- [ ] Visualisation
- [ ] Stretching

DAILY WHY

DATE

Today is my opportunity to:

What did I notice about my mindset today?

Breakfast

Snack am

Lunch

Snack pm

Dinner

WORKOUT

....

....

Today's wellness mantra

WEEKLY CHECK-IN

What goals have I achieved this week?

☐ Review My Wellness Goal Planner

☐ Review My Why Statement

☐ Complete My Weekly Planner

What's going well and why is it?

What's most challenging and how can I turn it to my advantage?

How can I drink more water every day?

What do I need to START doing to have better health?

What do I need to STOP doing for better health?

What is one thing I can do this week that will create the biggest results for my health & wellness?

OLD HABIT >	NEW HABIT >	NEW ACTIONS >	NEW AFFIRMATION / MANTRA

WEEKLY PLANNER

Shopping list:

NEW HEALTHY HABIT FOCUS

	BREAKFAST SNACK / WORKOUTS / CLASSES	LUNCH SNACK / WORKOUTS / CLASSES	DINNER SNACK / WORKOUTS / CLASSES
MONDAY			
TUESDAY			
WEDNESDAY			
THURSDAY			
FRIDAY			
SATURDAY			
SUNDAY			

DATE

DAILY WHY

HEALTH HABITS

☐ Meditation   ☐ 8 Glasses of water

☐ Visualisation   ☐ Stretching

Today is going to be great because:

What was today's lesson?

WORKOUT

....

....

Today's wellness mantra

Breakfast

Snack am

Lunch

Snack pm

Dinner

HEALTH HABITS

☐ Meditation   ☐ 8 Glasses of water

☐ Visualisation   ☐ Stretching

DAILY WHY

DATE

Today, I'm excited to create:

How did I show discipline and move closer to my wellness goals today?

Breakfast

Snack am

Lunch

Snack pm

Dinner

WORKOUT

....

....

Today's wellness mantra

DATE

DAILY WHY

HEALTH HABITS

☐ Meditation   ☐ 8 Glasses of water

☐ Visualisation   ☐ Stretching

Today, I'm going to focus on being:

What strengths did I use today?

WORKOUT

Breakfast

Snack am

Lunch

Today's wellness mantra

Snack pm

Dinner

☐ Meditation ☐ 8 Glasses of water

☐ Visualisation ☐ Stretching

DAILY WHY

DATE

Today would be amazing if:

Today, I practised mindfulness when:

Breakfast

Snack am

Lunch

Snack pm

Dinner

WORKOUT

Today's wellness mantra

DATE

HEALTH HABITS

- [ ] Meditation
- [ ] 8 Glasses of water
- [ ] Visualisation
- [ ] Stretching

Today, I'm open to the possibility of:

When did I show willpower today?

WORKOUT

....

....

Today's wellness mantra

Breakfast

Snack am

Lunch

Snack pm

Dinner

- [ ] Meditation
- [ ] 8 Glasses of water
- [ ] Visualisation
- [ ] Stretching

Today, I'm going to focus on eating:

What went well today?

Breakfast

Snack am

Lunch

Snack pm

Dinner

WORKOUT

....

....

Today's wellness mantra

WEEKLY CHECK-IN

My week in review

What progress have I made this week?

☐ Review My Wellness
Goal Planner

☐ Review My Why Statement

☐ Complete My Weekly Planner

Where do I see results & why?

What do I need to start or stop?

When do I feel the best in my body and mind?

What does my body need most, right now?

When and how do I sabotage my health and wellness goals?

What is one thing I can do this week that will create the biggest results for my health & wellness?

OLD HABIT >	NEW HABIT >	NEW ACTIONS >	NEW AFFIRMATION / MANTRA

WEEKLY PLANNER

Shopping list:

NEW HEALTHY HABIT FOCUS

	BREAKFAST SNACK / WORKOUTS / CLASSES	LUNCH SNACK / WORKOUTS / CLASSES	DINNER SNACK / WORKOUTS / CLASSES
MONDAY			
TUESDAY			
WEDNESDAY			
THURSDAY			
FRIDAY			
SATURDAY			
SUNDAY			

DAILY WHY

HEALTH HABITS

- [ ] Meditation
- [ ] 8 Glasses of water
- [ ] Visualisation
- [ ] Stretching

Today, I'm grateful for:

How did I feel in my body today and why?

WORKOUT

....

....

Today's wellness mantra

Breakfast

Snack am

Lunch

Snack pm

Dinner

- [ ] Meditation [ ] 8 Glasses of water
- [ ] Visualisation [ ] Stretching

DAILY WHY

DATE

My intention for today is:

What habits do I most want to improve and why?

Breakfast

Snack am

Lunch

Snack pm

Dinner

WORKOUT

Today's wellness mantra

DATE

HEALTH HABITS

☐ Meditation   ☐ 8 Glasses of water

☐ Visualisation   ☐ Stretching

What I love about my body is:

In what way did I practice conscious eating today?

WORKOUT

....

....

Today's wellness mantra

Breakfast

Snack am

Lunch

Snack pm

Dinner

- [ ] Meditation
- [ ] 8 Glasses of water
- [ ] Visualisation
- [ ] Stretching

DAILY WHY

DATE

Today is my opportunity to:

What did I notice about my mindset today?

Breakfast

Snack am

Lunch

Snack pm

Dinner

WORKOUT

Today's wellness mantra

DATE

DAILY WHY

HEALTH HABITS

☐ Meditation ☐ 8 Glasses of water

☐ Visualisation ☐ Stretching

Today is going to be great because:

What was today's lesson?

WORKOUT

....

....

Today's wellness mantra

Breakfast

Snack am

Lunch

Snack pm

Dinner

HEALTH HABITS

- [ ] Meditation
- [ ] 8 Glasses of water
- [ ] Visualisation
- [ ] Stretching

DAILY WHY

DATE

Today, I'm excited to create:

How did I show discipline and move closer to my wellness goals today?

Breakfast

Snack am

Lunch

Snack pm

Dinner

WORKOUT

Today's wellness mantra

WEEKLY CHECK-IN

My week in review

What major goals have I achieved this month?

☐ Review My Wellness Goal Planner

☐ Review My Why Statement

☐ Complete My Weekly Planner

Where am I having success and why?

What are the biggest distractions to improving my health and how can I remove them?

What does my body tell me I need to eat more or less of?

Do I eat too much or too little for a strong, healthy body?

What am I enjoying most about my journey to better health?

What is one thing I can do this week that will create the biggest results for my health & wellness?

OLD HABIT >	NEW HABIT >	NEW ACTIONS >	NEW AFFIRMATION / MANTRA

WEEKLY PLANNER

Shopping list:

NEW HEALTHY HABIT FOCUS

	BREAKFAST SNACK / WORKOUTS / CLASSES	LUNCH SNACK / WORKOUTS / CLASSES	DINNER SNACK / WORKOUTS / CLASSES
MONDAY			
TUESDAY			
WEDNESDAY			
THURSDAY			
FRIDAY			
SATURDAY			
SUNDAY			

☐ Meditation   ☐ 8 Glasses of water

☐ Visualisation   ☐ Stretching

Today, I'm going to focus on being:

What strengths did I use today?

WORKOUT

....

....

Today's wellness mantra

Breakfast

Snack am

Lunch

Snack pm

Dinner

HEALTH HABITS

☐ Meditation ☐ 8 Glasses of water

☐ Visualisation ☐ Stretching

DAILY WHY

DATE

Today would be amazing if:

Today, I practised mindfulness when:

Breakfast

Snack am

Lunch

Snack pm

Dinner

WORKOUT

....

....

Today's wellness mantra

DATE

DAILY WHY

HEALTH HABITS

☐ Meditation   ☐ 8 Glasses of water

☐ Visualisation   ☐ Stretching

Today, I'm open to the possibility of:

When did I show willpower today?

WORKOUT

....

....

Today's wellness mantra

Breakfast

Snack am

Lunch

Snack pm

Dinner

☐ Meditation   ☐ 8 Glasses of water

☐ Visualisation   ☐ Stretching

DAILY WHY

DATE

Today, I'm going to focus on eating:

What went well today?

| Breakfast |
| Snack am |
| Lunch |
| Snack pm |
| Dinner |

WORKOUT

....

....

Today's wellness mantra

DATE

DAILY WHY

HEALTH HABITS

☐ Meditation ☐ 8 Glasses of water

☐ Visualisation ☐ Stretching

Today, I'm grateful for:

How did I feel in my body today and why?

WORKOUT

....

....

Today's wellness mantra

Breakfast

Snack am

Lunch

Snack pm

Dinner

HEALTH HABITS

☐ Meditation   ☐ 8 Glasses of water

☐ Visualisation   ☐ Stretching

DAILY WHY

DATE

My intention for today is:

What habits do I most want to improve and why?

Breakfast

Snack am

Lunch

Snack pm

Dinner

WORKOUT

....

....

Today's wellness mantra

WEEKLY CHECK-IN

My week in review

What progress have I made this week?

☐ **Review My Wellness Goal Planner**

☐ **Review My Why Statement**

☐ **Complete My Weekly Planner**

What's working and why is it working?

What's not working and what am I willing to do about it?

What steps can I take to focus my diet on eating more fresh and healthy foods?

What is one thing I can do every day to take care of my body?

What three things do I most enjoy by improving my health?

What is one thing I can do this week that will create the biggest results for my health & wellness?

OLD HABIT >	NEW HABIT >	NEW ACTIONS >	NEW AFFIRMATION / MANTRA

WEEKLY PLANNER

Shopping list:

	BREAKFAST SNACK / WORKOUTS / CLASSES	LUNCH SNACK / WORKOUTS / CLASSES	DINNER SNACK / WORKOUTS / CLASSES
MONDAY			
TUESDAY			
WEDNESDAY			
THURSDAY			
FRIDAY			
SATURDAY			
SUNDAY			

DATE	DAILY WHY	HEALTH HABITS

HEALTH HABITS

☐ Meditation ☐ 8 Glasses of water

☐ Visualisation ☐ Stretching

What I love about my body is:

In what way did I practice conscious eating today?

WORKOUT

....

....

Today's wellness mantra

Breakfast

Snack am

Lunch

Snack pm

Dinner

HEALTH HABITS

☐ Meditation   ☐ 8 Glasses of water

☐ Visualisation ☐ Stretching

DAILY WHY

DATE

Today is my opportunity to:

What did I notice about my mindset today?

Breakfast

Snack am

Lunch

Snack pm

Dinner

WORKOUT

....

....

Today's wellness mantra

DAILY WHY

HEALTH HABITS

- [ ] Meditation
- [ ] 8 Glasses of water
- [ ] Visualisation
- [ ] Stretching

Today is going to be great because:

What was today's lesson?

WORKOUT

Breakfast

Snack am

Lunch

Today's wellness mantra

Snack pm

Dinner

☐ Meditation   ☐ 8 Glasses of water

☐ Visualisation   ☐ Stretching

DAILY WHY

DATE

Today, I'm excited to create:

How did I show discipline and move closer to my wellness goals today?

Breakfast

Snack am

Lunch

Snack pm

Dinner

WORKOUT

....

....

Today's wellness mantra

DATE

DAILY WHY

HEALTH HABITS

☐ Meditation ☐ 8 Glasses of water

☐ Visualisation ☐ Stretching

Today, I'm going to focus on being:

What strengths did I use today?

WORKOUT

....

....

Today's wellness mantra

Breakfast

Snack am

Lunch

Snack pm

Dinner

HEALTH HABITS

☐ Meditation   ☐ 8 Glasses of water

☐ Visualisation   ☐ Stretching

DAILY WHY

DATE

Today would be amazing if:

Today, I practised mindfulness when:

Breakfast

Snack am

Lunch

Snack pm

Dinner

WORKOUT

Today's wellness mantra

90 DAY REVIEW

What goals have I completed this past 90 days that have improved my health and wellness? How do I feel?

....

....

What's going well and why?
What mindset changes do I wish to make around my health and wellness?
What is no longer acceptable to me?

....

....

What do I need to STOP doing?

....

....

What do I need to START doing?

....

....

What limiting beliefs are holding me back from personal growth and better wellbeing?

....

....

What decisions do I need to make that I have been putting off around my health?

....

....

What activities do I spend my time on and how do they contribute to my health and wellness?

....

....

What new health goal am I focusing on for the next 90 days? What would I love to achieve?

....

....

....

- [ ] Review My Wellness Goal Planner
- [ ] Review My Why Statement
- [ ] Check My Healthy Habits
- [ ] Complete My 90 Day Planner
- [ ] Plan My Week
- [ ] Celebrate My Progress!

90 DAY PLANNER

Goal:

Target date:

Actions to complete this goal:

WHY I'D LOVE TO ACHIEVE THIS GOAL:

HOW WILL I FEEL WHEN I'VE REACHED THIS GOAL?

Goal:

Target date:

Actions to complete this goal:

WHY I'D LOVE TO ACHIEVE THIS GOAL:

HOW WILL I FEEL WHEN I'VE REACHED THIS GOAL?

Goal:

Target date:

Actions to complete this goal:

WHY I'D LOVE TO ACHIEVE THIS GOAL:

HOW WILL I FEEL WHEN I'VE REACHED THIS GOAL?

Goal:

Target date:

Actions to complete this goal:

WHY I'D LOVE TO ACHIEVE THIS GOAL:

HOW WILL I FEEL WHEN I'VE REACHED THIS GOAL?

TREAT YOUR BODY WITH KINDNESS.

WEEKLY PLANNER

Shopping list:

NEW HEALTHY HABIT FOCUS

	BREAKFAST SNACK / WORKOUTS / CLASSES	LUNCH SNACK / WORKOUTS / CLASSES	DINNER SNACK / WORKOUTS / CLASSES
MONDAY			
TUESDAY			
WEDNESDAY			
THURSDAY			
FRIDAY			
SATURDAY			
SUNDAY			

DATE

DAILY WHY

HEALTH HABITS

☐ Meditation   ☐ 8 Glasses of water

☐ Visualisation   ☐ Stretching

Today, I'm grateful for:

How did I feel in my body today and why?

WORKOUT

....

....

Today's wellness mantra

Breakfast

Snack am

Lunch

Snack pm

Dinner

HEALTH HABITS

- [ ] Meditation
- [ ] 8 Glasses of water
- [ ] Visualisation
- [ ] Stretching

DAILY WHY

DATE

My intention for today is:

What habits do I most want to improve and why?

Breakfast

Snack am

Lunch

Snack pm

Dinner

WORKOUT

....

....

Today's wellness mantra

DATE

DAILY WHY

HEALTH HABITS

☐ Meditation ☐ 8 Glasses of water

☐ Visualisation ☐ Stretching

What I love about my body is:

In what way did I practice conscious eating today?

WORKOUT

....

....

Today's wellness mantra

Breakfast

Snack am

Lunch

Snack pm

Dinner

- [ ] Meditation
- [ ] 8 Glasses of water
- [ ] Visualisation
- [ ] Stretching

DAILY WHY

DATE

Today is my opportunity to:

What did I notice about my mindset today?

Breakfast

Snack am

Lunch

Snack pm

Dinner

WORKOUT

....

....

Today's wellness mantra

DATE

DAILY WHY

HEALTH HABITS

☐ Meditation ☐ 8 Glasses of water

☐ Visualisation ☐ Stretching

Today is going to be great because:

What was today's lesson?

WORKOUT

....

....

Today's wellness mantra

Breakfast

Snack am

Lunch

Snack pm

Dinner

HEALTH HABITS

- [ ] Meditation
- [ ] 8 Glasses of water
- [ ] Visualisation
- [ ] Stretching

DAILY WHY

DATE

Today, I'm excited to create:

How did I show discipline and move closer to my wellness goals today?

Breakfast

Snack am

Lunch

Snack pm

Dinner

WORKOUT

....

....

Today's wellness mantra

WEEKLY CHECK-IN

My week in review

What goals have I achieved this week?

☐ Review My Wellness
   Goal Planner

☐ Review My Why Statement

☐ Complete My Weekly Planner

What's going well and why is it?

What's most challenging and how can I turn it to my advantage?

How can I drink more water every day?

What do I need to START doing to have better health?

What do I need to STOP doing for better health?

What is one thing I can do this week that will create the biggest results for my health & wellness?

OLD HABIT >	NEW HABIT >	NEW ACTIONS >	NEW AFFIRMATION / MANTRA

WEEKLY PLANNER

Shopping list:

NEW HEALTHY HABIT FOCUS

	BREAKFAST SNACK / WORKOUTS / CLASSES	LUNCH SNACK / WORKOUTS / CLASSES	DINNER SNACK / WORKOUTS / CLASSES
MONDAY			
TUESDAY			
WEDNESDAY			
THURSDAY			
FRIDAY			
SATURDAY			
SUNDAY			

☐ Meditation   ☐ 8 Glasses of water

☐ Visualisation   ☐ Stretching

Today, I'm going to focus on being:

What strengths did I use today?

WORKOUT

....

....

Today's wellness mantra

Breakfast

Snack am

Lunch

Snack pm

Dinner

- [ ] Meditation
- [ ] 8 Glasses of water
- [ ] Visualisation
- [ ] Stretching

DAILY WHY

DATE

Today would be amazing if:

Today, I practised mindfulness when:

Breakfast

Snack am

Lunch

Snack pm

Dinner

WORKOUT

....

....

Today's wellness mantra

DATE

DAILY WHY

HEALTH HABITS

☐ Meditation   ☐ 8 Glasses of water

☐ Visualisation   ☐ Stretching

Today, I'm open to the possibility of:

When did I show willpower today?

WORKOUT

....

....

Today's wellness mantra

Breakfast

Snack am

Lunch

Snack pm

Dinner

- [ ] Meditation
- [ ] 8 Glasses of water
- [ ] Visualisation
- [ ] Stretching

DAILY WHY

DATE

Today, I'm going to focus on eating:

What went well today?

Breakfast

Snack am

Lunch

Snack pm

Dinner

WORKOUT

....

....

Today's wellness mantra

DATE

HEALTH HABITS

- ☐ Meditation
- ☐ 8 Glasses of water
- ☐ Visualisation
- ☐ Stretching

Today, I'm grateful for:

How did I feel in my body today and why?

WORKOUT

....

....

Today's wellness mantra

Breakfast

Snack am

Lunch

Snack pm

Dinner

- [ ] Meditation
- [ ] 8 Glasses of water
- [ ] Visualisation
- [ ] Stretching

DAILY WHY

DATE

My intention for today is:

What habits do I most want to improve and why?

Breakfast

Snack am

Lunch

Snack pm

Dinner

WORKOUT

....

....

Today's wellness mantra

WEEKLY CHECK-IN

My week in review

What progress have I made this week?

☐ Review My Wellness
    Goal Planner

☐ Review My Why Statement

☐ Complete My Weekly Planner

Where do I see results & why?

What do I need to start or stop?

When do I feel the best in my body and mind?

What does my body need most, right now?

When and how do I sabotage my health and wellness goals?

What is one thing I can do this week that will create the biggest results for my health & wellness?

OLD HABIT >	NEW HABIT >	NEW ACTIONS >	NEW AFFIRMATION / MANTRA

WEEKLY PLANNER

Shopping list:

NEW HEALTHY HABIT FOCUS

	BREAKFAST SNACK / WORKOUTS / CLASSES	LUNCH SNACK / WORKOUTS / CLASSES	DINNER SNACK / WORKOUTS / CLASSES
MONDAY			
TUESDAY			
WEDNESDAY			
THURSDAY			
FRIDAY			
SATURDAY			
SUNDAY			

DATE

HEALTH HABITS

☐ Meditation   ☐ 8 Glasses of water

☐ Visualisation   ☐ Stretching

What I love about my body is:

In what way did I practice conscious eating today?

WORKOUT

....

....

Today's wellness mantra

Breakfast

Snack am

Lunch

Snack pm

Dinner

HEALTH HABITS

- [ ] Meditation
- [ ] 8 Glasses of water
- [ ] Visualisation
- [ ] Stretching

DAILY WHY

DATE

Today is my opportunity to:

What did I notice about my mindset today?

Breakfast

Snack am

Lunch

Snack pm

Dinner

WORKOUT

....

....

Today's wellness mantra

DATE

DAILY WHY

HEALTH HABITS

- [ ] Meditation
- [ ] 8 Glasses of water
- [ ] Visualisation
- [ ] Stretching

Today is going to be great because:

What was today's lesson?

WORKOUT

....

....

Today's wellness mantra

Breakfast

Snack am

Lunch

Snack pm

Dinner

☐ Meditation ☐ 8 Glasses of water

☐ Visualisation ☐ Stretching

DAILY WHY

DATE

Today, I'm excited to create:

How did I show discipline and move closer to my wellness goals today?

Breakfast

Snack am

Lunch

Snack pm

Dinner

WORKOUT

....

....

Today's wellness mantra

- [ ] Meditation
- [ ] 8 Glasses of water
- [ ] Visualisation
- [ ] Stretching

Today, I'm going to focus on being:

What strengths did I use today?

WORKOUT

....

....

Today's wellness mantra

Breakfast

Snack am

Lunch

Snack pm

Dinner

HEALTH HABITS

☐ Meditation ☐ 8 Glasses of water

☐ Visualisation ☐ Stretching

DAILY WHY

DATE

Today would be amazing if:

Today, I practised mindfulness when:

Breakfast

Snack am

Lunch

Snack pm

Dinner

WORKOUT

....

....

Today's wellness mantra

WEEKLY CHECK-IN

My week in review

What major goals have I achieved this month?

☐ Review My Wellness Goal Planner

☐ Review My Why Statement

☐ Complete My Weekly Planner

Where am I having success and why?

What are the biggest distractions to improving my health and how can I remove them?

What does my body tell me I need to eat more or less of?

Do I eat too much or too little for a strong, healthy body?

What am I enjoying most about my journey to better health?

What is one thing I can do this week that will create the biggest results for my health & wellness?

OLD HABIT >	NEW HABIT >	NEW ACTIONS >	NEW AFFIRMATION / MANTRA

WEEKLY PLANNER

Shopping list:

	BREAKFAST SNACK / WORKOUTS / CLASSES	LUNCH SNACK / WORKOUTS / CLASSES	DINNER SNACK / WORKOUTS / CLASSES
MONDAY			
TUESDAY			
WEDNESDAY			
THURSDAY			
FRIDAY			
SATURDAY			
SUNDAY			

DAILY WHY

HEALTH HABITS

☐ Meditation ☐ 8 Glasses of water

☐ Visualisation ☐ Stretching

Today, I'm open to the possibility of:

When did I show willpower today?

WORKOUT

....

....

Today's wellness mantra

Breakfast

Snack am

Lunch

Snack pm

Dinner

☐ Meditation ☐ 8 Glasses of water

☐ Visualisation ☐ Stretching

DAILY WHY

DATE

Today, I'm going to focus on eating:

What went well today?

Breakfast

Snack am

Lunch

Snack pm

Dinner

WORKOUT

....

....

Today's wellness mantra

DATE

HEALTH HABITS

☐ Meditation   ☐ 8 Glasses of water

☐ Visualisation   ☐ Stretching

Today, I'm grateful for:

How did I feel in my body today and why?

WORKOUT

....

....

Today's wellness mantra

Breakfast

Snack am

Lunch

Snack pm

Dinner

HEALTH HABITS

- [ ] Meditation
- [ ] Visualisation
- [ ] 8 Glasses of water
- [ ] Stretching

DAILY WHY

DATE

My intention for today is:

What habits do I most want to improve and why?

Breakfast

Snack am

Lunch

Snack pm

Dinner

WORKOUT

....

....

Today's wellness mantra

DATE

DAILY WHY

HEALTH HABITS

☐ Meditation ☐ 8 Glasses of water

☐ Visualisation ☐ Stretching

What I love about my body is:

In what way did I practice conscious eating today?

WORKOUT

....

....

Today's wellness mantra

Breakfast

Snack am

Lunch

Snack pm

Dinner

- [ ] Meditation
- [ ] 8 Glasses of water
- [ ] Visualisation
- [ ] Stretching

DAILY WHY

DATE

Today is my opportunity to:

What did I notice about my mindset today?

Breakfast

Snack am

Lunch

Snack pm

Dinner

WORKOUT

....

....

Today's wellness mantra

WEEKLY CHECK-IN

My week in review

What progress have I made this week?

☐ Review My Wellness
Goal Planner

☐ Review My Why Statement

☐ Complete My Weekly Planner

What's working and why is it working?

What's not working and what am I willing to do about it?

What steps can I take to focus my diet on eating more fresh and healthy foods?

What is one thing I can do every day to take care of my body?

What three things do I most enjoy by improving my health?

What is one thing I can do this week that will create the biggest results for my health & wellness?

OLD HABIT >	NEW HABIT >	NEW ACTIONS >	NEW AFFIRMATION / MANTRA

WEEKLY PLANNER

Shopping list:

	BREAKFAST SNACK / WORKOUTS / CLASSES	LUNCH SNACK / WORKOUTS / CLASSES	DINNER SNACK / WORKOUTS / CLASSES
MONDAY			
TUESDAY			
WEDNESDAY			
THURSDAY			
FRIDAY			
SATURDAY			
SUNDAY			

DATE

DAILY WHY

HEALTH HABITS

☐ Meditation   ☐ 8 Glasses of water

☐ Visualisation   ☐ Stretching

Today is going to be great because:

What was today's lesson?

WORKOUT

....

....

Today's wellness mantra

Breakfast

Snack am

Lunch

Snack pm

Dinner

- [ ] Meditation
- [ ] 8 Glasses of water
- [ ] Visualisation
- [ ] Stretching

Today, I'm excited to create:

How did I show discipline and move closer to my wellness goals today?

Breakfast

Snack am

Lunch

Snack pm

Dinner

WORKOUT

....

....

Today's wellness mantra

DATE

☐ Meditation   ☐ 8 Glasses of water

☐ Visualisation   ☐ Stretching

Today, I'm going to focus on being:

What strengths did I use today?

WORKOUT

....

....

Today's wellness mantra

Breakfast

Snack am

Lunch

Snack pm

Dinner

HEALTH HABITS

☐ Meditation   ☐ 8 Glasses of water

☐ Visualisation   ☐ Stretching

DAILY WHY

DATE

Today would be amazing if:

Today, I practised mindfulness when:

Breakfast

Snack am

Lunch

Snack pm

Dinner

WORKOUT

....

....

Today's wellness mantra

DATE

DAILY WHY

HEALTH HABITS

☐ Meditation   ☐ 8 Glasses of water

☐ Visualisation   ☐ Stretching

Today, I'm open to the possibility of:

When did I show willpower today?

WORKOUT

....

....

Today's wellness mantra

Breakfast

Snack am

Lunch

Snack pm

Dinner

☐ Meditation ☐ 8 Glasses of water

☐ Visualisation ☐ Stretching

Today, I'm going to focus on eating:

What went well today?

Breakfast

WORKOUT

Snack am

....

Lunch

....

Snack pm

Today's wellness mantra

Dinner

WEEKLY CHECK-IN

My week in review

What goals have I achieved this week?

☐ Review My Wellness Goal Planner

☐ Review My Why Statement

☐ Complete My Weekly Planner

What's going well and why is it?

What's most challenging and how can I turn it to my advantage?

How can I drink more water every day?

What do I need to START doing to have better health?

What do I need to STOP doing for better health?

What is one thing I can do this week that will create the biggest results for my health & wellness?

OLD HABIT >	NEW HABIT >	NEW ACTIONS >	NEW AFFIRMATION / MANTRA

WEEKLY PLANNER

Shopping list:

NEW HEALTHY HABIT FOCUS

	BREAKFAST SNACK / WORKOUTS / CLASSES	LUNCH SNACK / WORKOUTS / CLASSES	DINNER SNACK / WORKOUTS / CLASSES
MONDAY			
TUESDAY			
WEDNESDAY			
THURSDAY			
FRIDAY			
SATURDAY			
SUNDAY			

DATE

DAILY WHY

HEALTH HABITS

☐ Meditation ☐ 8 Glasses of water

☐ Visualisation ☐ Stretching

Today, I'm grateful for:

How did I feel in my body today and why?

WORKOUT

....

....

Today's wellness mantra

Breakfast

Snack am

Lunch

Snack pm

Dinner

HEALTH HABITS

- [ ] Meditation
- [ ] Visualisation
- [ ] 8 Glasses of water
- [ ] Stretching

DAILY WHY

DATE

My intention for today is:

What habits do I most want to improve and why?

Breakfast

Snack am

Lunch

Snack pm

Dinner

WORKOUT

....

....

Today's wellness mantra

- [ ] Meditation
- [ ] 8 Glasses of water
- [ ] Visualisation
- [ ] Stretching

What I love about my body is:

In what way did I practice conscious eating today?

WORKOUT

....

....

Today's wellness mantra

Breakfast

Snack am

Lunch

Snack pm

Dinner

- [ ] Meditation
- [ ] 8 Glasses of water
- [ ] Visualisation
- [ ] Stretching

DAILY WHY

DATE

Today is my opportunity to:

What did I notice about my mindset today?

Breakfast

Snack am

Lunch

Snack pm

Dinner

WORKOUT

....

....

Today's wellness mantra

DATE

HEALTH HABITS

- [ ] Meditation
- [ ] 8 Glasses of water
- [ ] Visualisation
- [ ] Stretching

Today is going to be great because:

What was today's lesson?

WORKOUT

....

....

Today's wellness mantra

Breakfast

Snack am

Lunch

Snack pm

Dinner

- [ ] Meditation
- [ ] 8 Glasses of water
- [ ] Visualisation
- [ ] Stretching

DAILY WHY

DATE

Today, I'm excited to create:

How did I show discipline and move closer to my wellness goals today?

Breakfast

Snack am

Lunch

Snack pm

Dinner

WORKOUT

....

....

Today's wellness mantra

WEEKLY CHECK-IN

My week in review

What progress have I made this week?

☐ Review My Wellness Goal Planner

☐ Review My Why Statement

☐ Complete My Weekly Planner

Where do I see results & why?

What do I need to start or stop?

When do I feel the best in my body and mind?

What does my body need most, right now?

When and how do I sabotage my health and wellness goals?

What is one thing I can do this week that will create the biggest results for my health & wellness?

OLD HABIT >	NEW HABIT >	NEW ACTIONS >	NEW AFFIRMATION / MANTRA

WEEKLY PLANNER

Shopping List:

	BREAKFAST SNACK / WORKOUTS / CLASSES	LUNCH SNACK / WORKOUTS / CLASSES	DINNER SNACK / WORKOUTS / CLASSES
MONDAY			
TUESDAY			
WEDNESDAY			
THURSDAY			
FRIDAY			
SATURDAY			
SUNDAY			

DATE	DAILY WHY	HEALTH HABITS

HEALTH HABITS

- [ ] Meditation
- [ ] 8 Glasses of water
- [ ] Visualisation
- [ ] Stretching

Today, I'm going to focus on being:

What strengths did I use today?

WORKOUT

....

....

Today's wellness mantra

Breakfast

Snack am

Lunch

Snack pm

Dinner

HEALTH HABITS

☐ Meditation   ☐ 8 Glasses of water

☐ Visualisation   ☐ Stretching

DAILY WHY

DATE

Today would be amazing if:

Today, I practised mindfulness when:

Breakfast

Snack am

Lunch

Snack pm

Dinner

WORKOUT

....

....

Today's wellness mantra

Meditation   8 Glasses of water

Visualisation   Stretching

Today, I'm open to the possibility of:

When did I show willpower today?

WORKOUT

....

....

Today's wellness mantra

Breakfast

Snack am

Lunch

Snack pm

Dinner

HEALTH HABITS

☐ Meditation ☐ 8 Glasses of water

☐ Visualisation ☐ Stretching

DAILY WHY

DATE

Today, I'm going to focus on eating:

What went well today?

Breakfast

Snack am

Lunch

Snack pm

Dinner

WORKOUT

....

....

Today's wellness mantra

DATE

DAILY WHY

HEALTH HABITS

☐ Meditation   ☐ 8 Glasses of water

☐ Visualisation   ☐ Stretching

Today, I'm grateful for:

How did I feel in my body today and why?

WORKOUT

....

....

Today's wellness mantra

Breakfast

Snack am

Lunch

Snack pm

Dinner

HEALTH HABITS

☐ Meditation ☐ 8 Glasses of water

☐ Visualisation ☐ Stretching

DAILY WHY

DATE

My intention for today is:

What habits do I most want to improve and why?

Breakfast

Snack am

Lunch

Snack pm

Dinner

WORKOUT

....

....

Today's wellness mantra

WEEKLY CHECK-IN

What major goals have I achieved this month?

☐ Review My Wellness Goal Planner

☐ Review My Why Statement

☐ Complete My Weekly Planner

Where am I having success and why?

What are the biggest distractions to improving my health and how can I remove them?

What does my body tell me I need to eat more or less of?

Do I eat too much or too little for a strong, healthy body?

What am I enjoying most about my journey to better health?

What is one thing I can do this week that will create the biggest results for my health & wellness?

OLD HABIT >	NEW HABIT >	NEW ACTIONS >	NEW AFFIRMATION / MANTRA

WEEKLY PLANNER

Shopping list:

	BREAKFAST SNACK / WORKOUTS / CLASSES	LUNCH SNACK / WORKOUTS / CLASSES	DINNER SNACK / WORKOUTS / CLASSES
MONDAY			
TUESDAY			
WEDNESDAY			
THURSDAY			
FRIDAY			
SATURDAY			
SUNDAY			

DAILY WHY

HEALTH HABITS

☐ Meditation ☐ 8 Glasses of water

☐ Visualisation ☐ Stretching

What I love about my body is:

In what way did I practice conscious eating today?

WORKOUT

....

....

Today's wellness mantra

Breakfast

Snack am

Lunch

Snack pm

Dinner

☐ Meditation   ☐ 8 Glasses of water

☐ Visualisation   ☐ Stretching

DATE

Today is my opportunity to:

What did I notice about my mindset today?

Breakfast

Snack am

Lunch

Snack pm

Dinner

WORKOUT

....

....

Today's wellness mantra

☐ Meditation   ☐ 8 Glasses of water

☐ Visualisation   ☐ Stretching

Today is going to be great because:

What was today's lesson?

WORKOUT

....

....

Today's wellness mantra

Breakfast

Snack am

Lunch

Snack pm

Dinner

HEALTH HABITS

☐ Meditation   ☐ 8 Glasses of water

☐ Visualisation   ☐ Stretching

DAILY WHY

DATE

Today, I'm excited to create:

How did I show discipline and move closer to my wellness goals today?

Breakfast

Snack am

Lunch

Snack pm

Dinner

WORKOUT

....

....

Today's wellness mantra

DATE	DAILY WHY	HEALTH HABITS

HEALTH HABITS

☐ Meditation   ☐ 8 Glasses of water

☐ Visualisation   ☐ Stretching

Today, I'm going to focus on being:

What strengths did I use today?

WORKOUT

....

....

Today's wellness mantra

Breakfast

Snack am

Lunch

Snack pm

Dinner

HEALTH HABITS

☐ Meditation   ☐ 8 Glasses of water

☐ Visualisation   ☐ Stretching

DAILY WHY

DATE

Today would be amazing if:

Today, I practised mindfulness when:

Breakfast

Snack am

Lunch

Snack pm

Dinner

WORKOUT

....

....

Today's wellness mantra

WEEKLY CHECK-IN

My week in review

What progress have I made this week?

☐ Review My Wellness
  Goal Planner

☐ Review My Why Statement

☐ Complete My Weekly Planner

What's working and why is it working?

What's not working and what am I willing to do about it?

What steps can I take to focus my diet on eating more fresh and healthy foods?

What is one thing I can do every day to take care of my body?

What three things do I most enjoy by improving my health?

What is one thing I can do this week that will create the biggest results for my health & wellness?

OLD HABIT >	NEW HABIT >	NEW ACTIONS >	NEW AFFIRMATION / MANTRA

WEEKLY PLANNER

Shopping list:

NEW HEALTHY HABIT FOCUS

	BREAKFAST SNACK / WORKOUTS / CLASSES	LUNCH SNACK / WORKOUTS / CLASSES	DINNER SNACK / WORKOUTS / CLASSES
MONDAY			
TUESDAY			
WEDNESDAY			
THURSDAY			
FRIDAY			
SATURDAY			
SUNDAY			

DATE

HEALTH HABITS

☐ Meditation   ☐ 8 Glasses of water

☐ Visualisation   ☐ Stretching

Today, I'm open to the possibility of:

When did I show willpower today?

WORKOUT

....

....

Today's wellness mantra

Breakfast

Snack am

Lunch

Snack pm

Dinner

- [ ] Meditation
- [ ] 8 Glasses of water
- [ ] Visualisation
- [ ] Stretching

DAILY WHY

DATE

Today, I'm going to focus on eating:

What went well today?

Breakfast

Snack am

Lunch

Snack pm

Dinner

WORKOUT

....

....

Today's wellness mantra

☐ Meditation ☐ 8 Glasses of water

☐ Visualisation ☐ Stretching

Today, I'm grateful for:

How did I feel in my body today and why?

WORKOUT

....

....

Today's wellness mantra

Breakfast

Snack am

Lunch

Snack pm

Dinner

- [ ] Meditation
- [ ] 8 Glasses of water
- [ ] Visualisation
- [ ] Stretching

DATE

My intention for today is:

What habits do I most want to improve and why?

Breakfast

Snack am

Lunch

Snack pm

Dinner

WORKOUT

....

....

Today's wellness mantra

☐ Meditation   ☐ 8 Glasses of water

☐ Visualisation   ☐ Stretching

What I love about my body is:

In what way did I practice conscious eating today?

WORKOUT

....

....

Today's wellness mantra

Breakfast

Snack am

Lunch

Snack pm

Dinner

HEALTH HABITS

☐ Meditation   ☐ 8 Glasses of water

☐ Visualisation   ☐ Stretching

DAILY WHY

DATE

Today is my opportunity to:

What did I notice about my mindset today?

Breakfast

Snack am

Lunch

Snack pm

Dinner

WORKOUT

....

....

Today's wellness mantra

WEEKLY CHECK-IN

My week in review

What goals have I achieved this week?

☐ Review My Wellness Goal Planner

☐ Review My Why Statement

☐ Complete My Weekly Planner

What's going well and why is it?

What's most challenging and how can I turn it to my advantage?

How can I drink more water every day?

What do I need to START doing to have better health?

What do I need to STOP doing for better health?

What is one thing I can do this week that will create the biggest results for my health & wellness?

OLD HABIT >	NEW HABIT >	NEW ACTIONS >	NEW AFFIRMATION / MANTRA

WEEKLY PLANNER

Shopping list:

NEW HEALTHY HABIT FOCUS

	BREAKFAST SNACK / WORKOUTS / CLASSES	LUNCH SNACK / WORKOUTS / CLASSES	DINNER SNACK / WORKOUTS / CLASSES
MONDAY			
TUESDAY			
WEDNESDAY			
THURSDAY			
FRIDAY			
SATURDAY			
SUNDAY			

DATE

DAILY WHY

HEALTH HABITS

☐ Meditation   ☐ 8 Glasses of water

☐ Visualisation   ☐ Stretching

Today is going to be great because:

What was today's lesson?

WORKOUT

....

....

Today's wellness mantra

Breakfast

Snack am

Lunch

Snack pm

Dinner

HEALTH HABITS

☐ Meditation ☐ 8 Glasses of water

☐ Visualisation ☐ Stretching

DAILY WHY

DATE

Today, I'm excited to create:

How did I show discipline and move closer to my wellness goals today?

Breakfast

Snack am

Lunch

Snack pm

Dinner

WORKOUT

....

....

Today's wellness mantra

DATE

HEALTH HABITS

- [ ] Meditation
- [ ] 8 Glasses of water
- [ ] Visualisation
- [ ] Stretching

Today, I'm going to focus on being:

What strengths did I use today?

WORKOUT

....

....

Today's wellness mantra

Breakfast

Snack am

Lunch

Snack pm

Dinner

- [ ] Meditation
- [ ] 8 Glasses of water
- [ ] Visualisation
- [ ] Stretching

DAILY WHY

DATE

Today would be amazing if:

Today, I practised mindfulness when:

Breakfast

Snack am

Lunch

Snack pm

Dinner

WORKOUT

....

....

Today's wellness mantra

DATE

HEALTH HABITS

- ☐ Meditation
- ☐ 8 Glasses of water
- ☐ Visualisation
- ☐ Stretching

Today, I'm open to the possibility of:

When did I show willpower today?

WORKOUT

....

....

Today's wellness mantra

Breakfast

Snack am

Lunch

Snack pm

Dinner

- [ ] Meditation
- [ ] 8 Glasses of water
- [ ] Visualisation
- [ ] Stretching

DAILY WHY

DATE

Today, I'm going to focus on eating:

What went well today?

Breakfast

Snack am

Lunch

Snack pm

Dinner

WORKOUT

....

....

Today's wellness mantra

WEEKLY CHECK-IN

What progress have I made this week?

☐ Review My Wellness Goal Planner

☐ Review My Why Statement

☐ Complete My Weekly Planner

Where do I see results & why?

What do I need to start or stop?

When do I feel the best in my body and mind?

What does my body need most, right now?

When and how do I sabotage my health and wellness goals?

What is one thing I can do this week that will create the biggest results for my health & wellness?

OLD HABIT >	NEW HABIT >	NEW ACTIONS >	NEW AFFIRMATION / MANTRA

WEEKLY PLANNER

Shopping list:

NEW HEALTHY HABIT FOCUS

	BREAKFAST SNACK / WORKOUTS / CLASSES	LUNCH SNACK / WORKOUTS / CLASSES	DINNER SNACK / WORKOUTS / CLASSES
MONDAY			
TUESDAY			
WEDNESDAY			
THURSDAY			
FRIDAY			
SATURDAY			
SUNDAY			

DATE

DAILY WHY

HEALTH HABITS

☐ Meditation ☐ 8 Glasses of water

☐ Visualisation ☐ Stretching

Today, I'm grateful for:

How did I feel in my body today and why?

WORKOUT

....

....

Today's wellness mantra

Breakfast

Snack am

Lunch

Snack pm

Dinner

☐ Meditation ☐ 8 Glasses of water

☐ Visualisation ☐ Stretching

DAILY WHY

DATE

My intention for today is:

What habits do I most want to improve and why?

Breakfast

Snack am

Lunch

Snack pm

Dinner

WORKOUT

....

....

Today's wellness mantra

DATE

DAILY WHY

HEALTH HABITS

☐ Meditation   ☐ 8 Glasses of water

☐ Visualisation   ☐ Stretching

What I love about my body is:

In what way did I practice conscious eating today?

WORKOUT

....

....

Today's wellness mantra

Breakfast

Snack am

Lunch

Snack pm

Dinner

Meditation

8 Glasses of water

Visualisation

Stretching

DAILY WHY

DATE

Today is my opportunity to:

What did I notice about my mindset today?

Breakfast

Snack am

Lunch

Snack pm

Dinner

WORKOUT

....

....

Today's wellness mantra

DATE

HEALTH HABITS

☐ Meditation ☐ 8 Glasses of water

☐ Visualisation ☐ Stretching

Today is going to be great because:

What was today's lesson?

WORKOUT

....

....

Today's wellness mantra

Breakfast

Snack am

Lunch

Snack pm

Dinner

HEALTH HABITS

☐ Meditation   ☐ 8 Glasses of water

☐ Visualisation   ☐ Stretching

DAILY WHY

DATE

Today, I'm excited to create:

How did I show discipline and move closer to my wellness goals today?

Breakfast

Snack am

Lunch

Snack pm

Dinner

WORKOUT

....

....

Today's wellness mantra

WEEKLY CHECK-IN

My week in review

What major goals have I achieved this month?

☐ Review My Wellness Goal Planner

☐ Review My Why Statement

☐ Complete My Weekly Planner

Where am I having success and why?

What are the biggest distractions to improving my health and how can I remove them?

What does my body tell me I need to eat more or less of?

Do I eat too much or too little for a strong, healthy body?

What am I enjoying most about my journey to better health?

What is one thing I can do this week that will create the biggest results for my health & wellness?

OLD HABIT >	NEW HABIT >	NEW ACTIONS >	NEW AFFIRMATION / MANTRA

WEEKLY PLANNER

Shopping list:

NEW HEALTHY HABIT FOCUS

	BREAKFAST SNACK / WORKOUTS / CLASSES	LUNCH SNACK / WORKOUTS / CLASSES	DINNER SNACK / WORKOUTS / CLASSES
MONDAY			
TUESDAY			
WEDNESDAY			
THURSDAY			
FRIDAY			
SATURDAY			
SUNDAY			

DATE

HEALTH HABITS

☐ Meditation   ☐ 8 Glasses of water

☐ Visualisation   ☐ Stretching

Today, I'm going to focus on being:

What strengths did I use today?

WORKOUT

....

....

Today's wellness mantra

Breakfast

Snack am

Lunch

Snack pm

Dinner

Meditation ☐   8 Glasses of water ☐

Visualisation ☐   Stretching ☐

Today would be amazing if:

Today, I practised mindfulness when:

Breakfast

Snack am

Lunch

Snack pm

Dinner

WORKOUT

....

....

Today's wellness mantra

DATE

DAILY WHY

HEALTH HABITS

Meditation ☐   ☐ 8 Glasses of water

Visualisation ☐   ☐ Stretching

Today, I'm open to the possibility of:

When did I show willpower today?

WORKOUT

....

....

Today's wellness mantra

Breakfast

Snack am

Lunch

Snack pm

Dinner

☐ Meditation   ☐ 8 Glasses of water

☐ Visualisation   ☐ Stretching

DAILY WHY

DATE

Today, I'm going to focus on eating:

What went well today?

Breakfast

Snack am

Lunch

Snack pm

Dinner

WORKOUT

Today's wellness mantra

DATE

DAILY WHY

HEALTH HABITS

- [ ] Meditation
- [ ] 8 Glasses of water
- [ ] Visualisation
- [ ] Stretching

Today, I'm grateful for:

How did I feel in my body today and why?

WORKOUT

....

....

Today's wellness mantra

Breakfast

Snack am

Lunch

Snack pm

Dinner

HEALTH HABITS

☐ Meditation   ☐ 8 Glasses of water

☐ Visualisation   ☐ Stretching

DAILY WHY

DATE

My intention for today is:

What habits do I most want to improve and why?

Breakfast

Snack am

Lunch

Snack pm

Dinner

WORKOUT

....

....

Today's wellness mantra

WEEKLY CHECK-IN

My week in review

What progress have I made this week?

☐ Review My Wellness Goal Planner

☐ Review My Why Statement

☐ Complete My Weekly Planner

What's working and why is it working?

What's not working and what am I willing to do about it?

What steps can I take to focus my diet on eating more fresh and healthy foods?

What is one thing I can do every day to take care of my body?

What three things do I most enjoy by improving my health?

What is one thing I can do this week that will create the biggest results for my health & wellness?

OLD HABIT >	NEW HABIT >	NEW ACTIONS >	NEW AFFIRMATION / MANTRA

WEEKLY PLANNER

Shopping list:

	BREAKFAST SNACK / WORKOUTS / CLASSES	LUNCH SNACK / WORKOUTS / CLASSES	DINNER SNACK / WORKOUTS / CLASSES
MONDAY			
TUESDAY			
WEDNESDAY			
THURSDAY			
FRIDAY			
SATURDAY			
SUNDAY			

DATE

DAILY WHY

HEALTH HABITS

☐ Meditation   ☐ 8 Glasses of water

☐ Visualisation   ☐ Stretching

What I love about my body is:

In what way did I practice conscious eating today?

WORKOUT

....

....

Today's wellness mantra

Breakfast

Snack am

Lunch

Snack pm

Dinner

HEALTH HABITS

☐ Meditation   ☐ 8 Glasses of water

☐ Visualisation   ☐ Stretching

DAILY WHY

DATE

Today is my opportunity to:

What did I notice about my mindset today?

Breakfast

Snack am

Lunch

Snack pm

Dinner

WORKOUT

....

....

Today's wellness mantra

DATE

DAILY WHY

HEALTH HABITS

☐ Meditation   ☐ 8 Glasses of water

☐ Visualisation   ☐ Stretching

Today is going to be great because:

What was today's lesson?

WORKOUT

....

....

Today's wellness mantra

Breakfast

Snack am

Lunch

Snack pm

Dinner

HEALTH HABITS

- [ ] Meditation
- [ ] Visualisation
- [ ] 8 Glasses of water
- [ ] Stretching

DAILY WHY

DATE

Today, I'm excited to create:

How did I show discipline and move closer to my wellness goals today?

Breakfast

Snack am

Lunch

Snack pm

Dinner

WORKOUT

....

....

Today's wellness mantra

DATE

HEALTH HABITS

- [ ] Meditation
- [ ] 8 Glasses of water
- [ ] Visualisation
- [ ] Stretching

Today, I'm going to focus on being:

What strengths did I use today?

WORKOUT

....

....

Today's wellness mantra

Breakfast

Snack am

Lunch

Snack pm

Dinner

HEALTH HABITS

- [ ] Meditation
- [ ] 8 Glasses of water
- [ ] Visualisation
- [ ] Stretching

DAILY WHY

DATE

Today would be amazing if:

Today, I practised mindfulness when:

Breakfast

Snack am

Lunch

Snack pm

Dinner

WORKOUT

....

....

Today's wellness mantra

YEARLY REVIEW

IF YOU'VE MADE IT TO THIS POINT IN THE JOURNAL, IT'S LIKELY YOU'VE GONE THROUGH AN INCREDIBLE PERSONAL TRANSFORMATION. CONGRATULATIONS ON YOUR AMAZING COMMITMENT, DISCIPLINE AND FOCUS. NOW IT'S TIME TO REFLECT BACK OVER YOUR YEAR AND NOTE YOUR ACHIEVEMENTS, YOUR LESSONS, YOUR CHALLENGES AND YOUR BREAKTHROUGHS, AND CELEBRATE HOW FAR YOU'VE COME!

USE THESE OBSERVATIONS AS STEPPING-STONES TO CATAPULT YOU INTO ANOTHER YEAR OF GREATNESS.

HELP US TO SPREAD OUR TRANSFORMATIONAL JOURNALS BY SHARING YOUR IMAGES USING #DAILYGREATNESSJOURNAL ON SOCIAL MEDIA OR REVIEW THE DAILYGREATNESS JOURNAL ON OUR WEBSITE OR ON AMAZON AND GO IN OUR MONTHLY DRAW TO WIN A FREE COPY!

TO REORDER YOUR DAILYGREATNESS JOURNAL AND BROWSE ALL OUR OTHER JOURNALS, ONLINE COURSES AND CONTENT, VISIT DAILYGREATNESSJOURNAL.COM.

- [ ] REVIEW MY WELLNESS GOAL PLANNER

- [ ] REVIEW MY WHY STATEMENT

- [ ] REVIEW MY YEARLY PLANNER

- [ ] CELEBRATE MY ACHIEVEMENTS!

- [ ] CREATE NEW WELLNESS GOALS FOR NEXT YEAR

What major health goals have I achieved this past year?

How would I describe how I feel? How much closer am I to feeling how I want to feel?

What new empowered habits have I adopted this year?

How am I embracing my new healthy lifestyle?

What breakthroughs have I had?

How has my overall attitude changed since using the Dailygreatness Wellness Journal?

What have I enjoyed most about the past year?

What challenges have I faced and overcome?

How has my energy and general enthusiasm for life changed?

What have I learned about myself?

How have my relationships improved since I started focusing on my health more?

What areas of my health would I still like to work on next year?

What decisions do I need to make around my health before moving into another year?

What major wellness goals will I focus on next year?